365

Stories for Girls

Reprinted in 2017

An imprint of Om Books International

Corporate & Editorial Office
A 12, Sector 64, Noida 201 301
Uttar Pradesh, India
Phone: +91 120 477 4100
Email: editorial@ombooks.com
Website: www.ombooksinternational.com

Sales Office
107, Ansari Road, Darya Ganj,
New Delhi 110 002, India
Phone: +91 11 4000 9000
Fax: +91 11 2327 8091
Email: sales@ombooks.com
Website: www.ombooks.com

ISBN: 978-93-80070-84-1

Printed in India

1 0 9 8 7 6 5

365
Stories
for
Girls

Om
KIDZ
An imprint of Om Books International

Contents

APRIL

MAY

JUN

JULY

AUGUST

SEPTEMBER

OCTOBER

NOVEMBER

DECEMBER

1. The Fisherman and His Wife

Once, a Fisherman lived with his Wife in a pigsty. One day, while fishing, he caught a big fish. It said, "I am not a Fish, but an enchanted prince. Please let me go." The Fisherman felt sorry and let it go.

However, his Wife wanted him to ask the Fish to give them a hut. The Fisherman did so, and the Fish granted her wish. Thereafter, the Wife wanted a big castle. The Fish granted that wish, too.

The Wife, next, wanted to be the Queen. So, the Fish made her the Queen. The Wife then, said, "I want to be the Empress of this kingdom." The Fish fulfilled her wish.

Then, the Wife said, "I wish to be God." When the Fisherman went to the Fish with this request, it said, "That is impossible! She is only fit to live in a pigsty!" Thus, the Fisherman and his Wife continued to live in a pigsty all their life!

2. The Three Spinners

Once, a lovely Girl had many good qualities but she disliked spinning yarn! One day, her Mother scolded her and she wept. The Queen heard the cries and asked, "Who makes this Girl cry?"

The Girl's Mother was ashamed to say that her daughter disliked spinning. Hence she lied, "Oh! My Girl loves spinning, but I'm poor and cannot buy enough flax."

The Queen said, "That should not be a problem. Send her to me. I love the sound of the humming wheel!"

The Queen then brought the Girl to her palace and gave her plenty of flax. She told the Girl that if she spun it all, she could marry the Prince.

The Girl cried on seeing the huge amount of flax, "Oh! I will have to spin so much flax, when I have never spun!" Just then, she saw three women. One of them had a broad foot. The second had a big lower lip that hung till the chin. The third woman had a large thumb.

The three women said, "We shall help you, only if you promise to invite us to your wedding." The Girl agreed and the three women finished spinning the entire flax.

The wedding day was here! The Girl said to the Prince, "I have three Aunts who'd like to join us for the feast."

The three Spinners arrived. The Prince was shocked, "Ah! How do you have such peculiar features?"

The first Spinner, with the broad foot, replied, "I've been treading the spinning wheel!" The second Spinner, with the big lower lip said, "I've been licking the flax!" The last Spinner, with a big thumb said, "I've been twisting the thread for years!"

The Prince remarked, "Oh! If that's the result of spinning, then my wife shall never spin again."

The Girl had kept her promise, thus, she never had to spin again in her life!

3. The Golden Bird

Once, a King had an apple tree which bore golden apples in his royal garden. One day, the King realised that somebody stole his apples every day. He told his Elder Son to guard the apples at night. However, the Elder Son fell asleep and another apple was stolen.

Then, he sent his Second Son to guard the garden, who slept too and an apple was stolen again. Then one of his Ministers suggested that the King should send his Youngest Son. The King said, "My Youngest Son is good for nothing."

The Minister argued, "One should never underestimate anybody. Give him a chance."

The King agreed and sent his Youngest Son to guard the garden. The Son kept awake all night and caught the Golden Bird that stole the apples every day.

The King was delighted to see the beautiful Golden Bird and thanked his son. After this, he never underestimated anybody.

4. Frau Trude

There was once a stubborn young Girl, who never obeyed her parents. One day, the Girl wanted to meet a woman known as Frau Trude. However, the Girl's parents felt that Frau Trude was a wicked woman. They stopped her from meeting Frau Trude.

The Girl did not listen to them and went to Frau Trude's house. There, she saw a black coal miner, a green man who was a hunter and a red man who was a butcher. And Frau Trude seemed to look like the devil herself! So the Girl told Frau Trude about her fears.

Frau Trude laughed and said that she had wanted the girl from a long time. Then, turning her into a block of wood, Frau Trude threw it into the fire. She then warmed herself by the fire, happy that it was burning very brightly!

5. The Crystal Ball

Once, there was an Enchantress, who casted spells. She feared that her three sons would steal her powers. Thus, she changed her Eldest Son into an eagle and Second into a whale. The Youngest Son escaped. He wanted to free the King's Daughter, who was imprisoned in a castle. On his way, two giants gave the Youngest Son a magical cap. He put it on, and immediately reached the castle.

There, the Princess told him that an Enchanter had made her ugly, and she would be free only if he brings a crystal ball to the Enchanter. The Youngest Son obtained the crystal ball by defeating a violent bull and a fiery eagle with the help of his Eagle and Whale brothers. With the crystal ball, the Youngest Son destroyed the Enchanter and also freed his brothers from their curse. He then married the Princess and became the King of the castle.

6. Maid Maleen

When Maleen insisted on marrying the Prince she loved, her father imprisoned her in a dark castle for seven years. However, she escaped by digging through the castle wall. Once outside, she saw that her father's kingdom had been destroyed.

Finally, after a long journey, she found a job as a maid in a palace. It was the palace of the Prince she loved. He was soon to be married to a Princess. But the Princess was very ugly and wicked. She forced Maleen to pose as the bride because she didn't want the Prince to see her ugliness.

After the wedding, when the Prince saw the ugly Princess in his room, he exclaimed, "Where is my bride? You certainly are not!" The wicked Princess became angry and tried to kill Maleen. Maleen cried for help and told the Prince about her true identity. The Prince was overjoyed and, they were, at last, united.

7. The Gold-Children

Once, a poor Fisherman caught a magical fish. The fish gave him two Gold Children and two Golden Lilies. It told him that the Lilies would bloom if the Children were safe.

The Gold Children soon grew up and left home. People laughed at them as they were made of gold. One of the Gold Children became sad and returned home. The other went on his journey. Soon, he married a beautiful lady.

One day, the Gold Boy went to the forest for hunting. There, he was chasing a stag when he met a Witch. The Witch turned him into stone. The other Gold Boy saw that one of the Lilies was dying. He understood that his brother was in danger. He set out to save him Soon, he reached the forest and found the evil Witch. He forced her to bring his brother back to life. The brothers returned home happily.

8. The Mouse, the Bird and the Sausage

Once, a Mouse, a Bird and a Sausage lived together. The Bird gathered firewood. The Mouse carried water, lit the fire and laid the table. The Sausage was the cook.

One day, the Bird met another bird, who said, "The others have such easy tasks. Your work is the most difficult!"

The Bird told the others, "Let's divide the housework differently." Thus, gathering firewood became the Sausage's task. The Mouse became the cook and the Bird was to fetch water.

When the Sausage went to fetch firewood, a dog ate it up. Meanwhile, at home, the Mouse tried to mix the vegetables, as the Sausage did, by rolling in the pot. However, she was burnt to death.

When the Bird could not find the Mouse, he threw the burnt wood all around in panic. The house caught fire. When the Bird went to the well to fetch water, she drowned. It is better to do what one is good at, and not listen to foolish advice!

9. The Curse

Once, a King and a Queen had twelve sons. The King was cursed that when his thirteenth child was born, he would kill all his sons. Thus, when the Queen gave birth to a girl, she sent her sons to hide in the forest. However, the Princess grew up and went to live in the forest with her brothers.

One day, the Princess mistakenly plucked twelve magical flowers from the garden. Her brothers at once turned into birds. Just then, she heard a voice, "If you want your brothers back, remain silent for seven years."

One day, a King saw the beautiful Princess and married her. The King's stepmother was a cruel woman. She planned to kill the new queen. Just then the seven years also ended and the Princess' brothers were free from the spell. They came and killed the wicked stepmother. Thereafter, they all lived happily together.

10. The Singing, Soaring Lark

Once, a Man had three daughters. One day, he set out on a long journey. He promised to bring pearls and diamonds for the two elder girls. The youngest asked for a singing, soaring Lark. When it was time to return home, the Man could not find a lark. Then, he spotted one in a forest.

As the Man tried to catch it, a Lion, guarding the Lark, sprang towards him. The Lion allowed the Man to take the Lark on one condition. The Man would have to send him its feathers with his daughter.

Unhappy, the Man went home to his youngest daughter. He told her of the Lion's order. The Girl smiled, fearlessly. The next morning, she went into the forest. She kept the Lark's feathers before the Lion. Magically, he turned into a Prince. He had been under a spell. The grateful Prince married the youngest daughter.

11. The Goose-Girl

Once, there was a beautiful Girl with golden hair. She helped a young boy, Conrad, to look after the Prince's geese.

One day, they took the geese to a meadow. The Girl went behind a tree and combed her hair. Conrad saw her and bent to pluck a few strands of her hair.

The Girl at once called aloud for a strong wind. The wind came and blew away Conrad's cap. He ran after it. Meanwhile, the Girl quickly braided her hair.

That evening, Conrad went to the Prince and told him about the Girl's golden hair. The Prince was curious. Thus, he followed her the next day. He heard her tell the geese that she was actually a Princess, from a neighbouring kingdom. She had promised her dying mother that she would not tell anyone her true identity.

The Prince took the Princess to his castle and soon married her.

12. Sweet Porridge

Once, a Girl lived with her Mother. They were very poor and had nothing to eat. One evening, the Girl met an Old Lady who gave her a little pot and said, "Take this pot and say, 'cook little pot,' it will cook good sweet porridge. To stop it, say, 'stop little pot.'"

The Girl went home and tried the pot. The pot was soon full of sweet porridge. The Girl and her Mother ate happily. Then, one day the Girl had gone out, when her Mother said to the pot, "cook little pot". The pot cooked sweet porridge, and she ate it.

She forgot what to say to the pot to stop cooking. So the pot continued cooking till it split over and reached the street. Everyone in the village was scared.

Finally, the Girl returned and said, "stop little pot." The pot stopped cooking at once!

13. The Frog Prince

Once, there lived a King who had a beautiful daughter. One day, the Princess was playing in the forest when her ball fell in a fountain. Suddenly a Frog came out and said, "I will get your ball. But you will have to love me, in return."

The Princess agreed. Just as the Frog got her ball, the Princess ran away.

The next day, the Frog reached the King's palace. He told the King about the Princess' promise. The King said, "My dear, the Frog helped you, now you should fulfill your promise."

Thus, the Frog started living with the Princess. With time, she started liking him a lot. Then, one day, the Frog changed into a handsome Prince. He said, "A curse had changed me into a Frog. Your love has broken that curse."

The Princess was very happy. Soon, they both were married and lived happily ever after.

14. The Girl and the Toad

Once upon a time, there lived a little Girl with her mother. Every afternoon her mother gave her a bowl of milk and bread. The little Girl would go to the garden and share her lunch with a Toad. The Toad would dip its head into the bowl. This gave the little Girl great joy. Soon, it started bringing pretty playthings for the Girl.

One day, the Toad drank only milk. Then the Girl said, "Eat the bread as well my friend."

The Girl's mother was standing in the kitchen and heard her child talking to someone. Then she saw the Toad and ran out with a ladle. She struck the Toad dead with the ladle.

From that day the Girl was sad and missed her friend. So long as the Toad had eaten with her, she had grown well. Soon she started getting weak and one day she fell sick. Her mother then realized that her daughter was missing her friend. She got her a little kitten. The Girl was happy again!

15. The Toad

Once upon a time, there lived a little Toad in the garden. Every day some children would come to the garden to play. One day, the children were playing hide-n-seek. A Child was looking for her sister who was hiding.

Suddenly the Toad peeped from his hole. The Child saw the little head come out and go back in. So the Child called out, "Come out little Toad." The Toad was scared but slowly made its way up. Then the Child went up to it and asked, "Have you seen my sister in red stockings?

"The Toad shook its head and said, "Have you?" And the Child said, "No I have not, have you?" They kept on talking like this for some time, till the child realized what the Toad was actually saying!

The Toad said "Huhu huhu huhu," and went back into his hole. Meanwhile, the Child's sister appeared.

16. Little Briar Rose

A King and Queen threw a banquet at the birth of their daughter. Many wise women were called to bless the child but one was left out. In her anger, she cursed the child with death in her fifteenth year but another wise woman changed it to sleep for a hundred years.

As foretold, in her fifteenth year, the child fell into a deep sleep, which extended over the entire kingdom. Thorns grew around the castle, which would not allow anyone inside, while Briar Rose as the little girl was known slept.

One day, when the hundred years had come to an end and the thorns had turned to flowers, a young Prince entered the castle and kissed Briar Rose. Immediately, she and all the others in the castle were awakened and there were great celebrations. Briar Rose and the Prince were married and all lived happily ever after.

17. St. Joseph's Gift

Once, a woman had three daughters. The Eldest was wicked, the Second much better and the Youngest good. The Mother, however, hated the Youngest and sent her off into the forest.

The Youngest daughter roamed around in the forest and finally reached St. Joseph's hut at sunset. She gave most of her food to him to eat. Then, she slept on the ground. St. Joseph rewarded her with a huge sack of money.

She went back home happy. The next day, the Second daughter went to St. Joseph's hut. She gave him some food and shared his bed. She was rewarded with a small sack of money.

Then, the greedy Eldest daughter went to the hut. She ate all the food and made St. Joseph sleep on the floor. There was, of course, no reward for her. On the way, scorpions and snakes stung her to death.

18. The Rose

There was once a poor widow who had a daughter. The Girl often had to go to the forest to fetch firewood. Once, she went deep into the forest. There, a handsome young Boy came to her and helped her pick up the wood. However, the strange Boy soon disappeared.

When the Girl told her Mother about this incident, she did not believe it.

Some days later, the Girl went to the forest and brought home a rose. She told her Mother that the strange Boy had given her this rose and said that when it was in full bloom, he would return. The Mother put the rose in water.

One morning, the Mother found her daughter lying dead on her bed. However, she was smiling and looking very happy. Just then, the Mother saw that the rose was in full bloom!

19. The Bleeding Loaf

Once, there were two sisters. One was a Rich Woman with no children and the other was a Poor Widow who had five children. The Poor Widow went to the Rich Woman to ask for food for her children. However, the Rich Woman rudely chased her away.

After some time, the Rich Woman's husband returned home. When he tried to cut a piece of bread, blood flowed out of the bread. The Rich Woman was terrified and told him what had occurred. He rushed to help the Poor Widow.

He saw that three of the Poor Widow's children were dead, and she was praying with her two youngest children in her arms.

He offered her food. However, she answered, "God will satisfy our hunger now." As soon as she said this, the two little ones drew their last breath. At this, the Poor Widow's heart broke, and she fell down dead.

Henceforth, the Rich Woman and her husband decided to share their riches with the poor.

20. God's Justice

Once, there lived a lonely Old Woman. All her loved ones were dead. She was very sad and blamed God for her loss. One night, the Old Woman could not sleep and sat thinking about her two dead sons. When the church bells rang for prayer, the Old Woman got ready and went to the church. When she reached the church, she was surprised to see it filled with a strange glow.

Suddenly, she realized that the people sitting in the church were her dead relatives! By the altar, she saw her two sons. One was hanging on the gallows, and the other bound to the wheel. One of her dead aunts said, "That would have been the fate of your sons if they had lived!"

The Old Woman thanked God for having dealt with her more kindly than she had been able to understand. Soon after, she died peacefully.

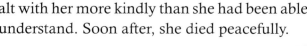

21. The Hazel-Branch

One afternoon, as the infant Jesus fell asleep in his cradle. His Mother decided to get some strawberries for him. In the woods outside, she found a spot with the most delicious looking strawberries. However, as she bent to pick one strawberry, a snake sprang up out of the grass. She got very scared. She left the strawberries and ran away. However, the snake darted after her. In order to escape from the snake, she hid herself behind a Hazel-bush.

She stayed there until the snake had crept away. Then she went back and gathered the strawberries. As she set out on her way home she said, "The Hazel-bush saved me today. May it protect other people as well!" Therefore, from the most ancient times, people have believed that a green Hazel-branch will protect them against snakes and everything else that creeps on the earth.

22. The Raven

One day, a Man was walking through a forest. As, he sat under a tree to rest, a Raven started talking to him. She narrated her tale, sadly. She was a Princess trapped under a spell. To free her, the Man had to rescue her from a castle at Stormberg. Then, she flew away, leaving him with a ring.

The Man searched far and wide. At last, he found the castle on a glass mountain. He slipped as he tried to climb it. Disappointed, he entered a cave near the mountain. There, he saw a bag. The bag had magic boots and a stick. He walked up the mountain in the boots. He opened the door by knocking on it with the stick. He found a beautiful maiden sitting inside. Joyfully, he gave her the ring. The spell was broken. The Princes married the Man and they lived happily thereafter.

23. The Three Little Birds

Once, there lived a King and Queen. They eagerly awaited the birth of their child. Just then, the Queen's two Sisters came to live with them. One day, the King had to go away. The Queen had a baby boy. The Sisters were envious of the Queen. Therefore, they quietly took the baby and dropped him in the river. Three little Birds appeared before them and sang out, "You will pay for your cruel act!"

The wicked Sisters told the King that the baby had died. However, a fisherman had rescued the baby boy. He lovingly cared for the child, as his own son.

After some years, the King went to the forest. The three little Birds flew before him. Then, they told him the tale of his lost child. The King rushed to the fisherman's hut and met his son. He took him back to his kingdom. He also punished the Queen's sisters.

24. The Elves

There was once a King. He was very sad, as his beautiful Daughter had disappeared mysteriously.

The King announced that whoever found the Princess would get a reward.

Hans, a young man, set out to find the Princess. After walking for days, he reached a castle, where he met tiny Elves. When he told them about the Princess, the kind Elves told Hans to go down the old well in the castle. They gave Hans a flute.

Hans soon found the well and climbed down. Inside the well, there was a chamber with a door in the corner. Behind the door was the lost Princess. A Dragon had caught and imprisoned her.

Hans killed the Dragon. Then, he played the flute. The Elves magically appeared before them. They carried them both out of the well and to the King's palace.

Hans and the Princess were soon married and lived happily ever after.

25. The Louse and the Flea

A Louse and a Flea lived together. One day, the Louse burnt herself. Seeing this, the Flea began to scream. The Door asked the Flea what happened. The Flea replied, "The Louse burnt herself." The Door felt so sad that he started creaking.

The Broom heard him and asked, "Why are you creaking?" When the Door told her, she began to sweep.

A Cart saw the Broom and asked, "Why are you sweeping?" The Broom explained and the Cart started running. Looking at that, an Ash Heap soon started burning; and looking at that, a Tree started shaking.

Finally, a Girl asked the Tree, "Why are you shaking?" The Tree told her and the Girl decided to break her water jug. The water that flowed out of the jug asked her why she broke the jug. She explained, and the water called all its other cousins. Soon, a lot of water flowed and drowned them all. What a lousy waste!

26. The Lambkin and the Little Fish

Once, a Brother and Sister lived with their Stepmother, who was a witch. She treated them very badly. One day, the Stepmother turned the Brother into a Fish and the Sister into a Lamb through her magic. Then she kept the Fish in the pond and the Lamb in the coop.

The next evening, some guests came at the wicked Stepmother's house. She ordered her Cook to kill the Lamb and make a meal for them. The moment the Cook tried to kill the Lamb, she cried to her brother in the pond. Hearing the human voice, the Cook understood that they were the creation of the wicked witch. Therefore, he cooked some other lamb and secretly took the lamb and the fish away to a good lady in the village.

The good lady took them both to a wise woman who turned them into humans again. From then on, the Brother and the Sister lived happily with the good lady.

27. The Clever Tailor

Once, there lived a beautiful but proud Princess. Whoever came to marry her, the Princess would give them a riddle to solve. She had announced that whoever solved it, could marry her.

One day, a Tailor offered the Princess a marriage proposal. The Princess asked, "I have two kinds of hair on my head. What are their colours?" The Tailor was very clever. He thought and said, "You have silver and golden coloured hair."

He was right but the proud Princess said, "You have to spend a night with a Bear. If you are still alive in the morning, you shall marry me." Now, the Bear had killed all the earlier suitors. However, the Tailor was well prepared. He kept the Bear distracted all night. Then, finally he tricked him by tying him up.

In the morning, the proud Princess accepted her defeat. She was soon married to the clever Tailor.

28. The Peasant's Wise Daughter

Once, there lived a King, whose wife was once a Peasant's Daughter. One day, the King settled a quarrel between two Peasants. One of the Peasants found the King's decision unfair, thus, he went to the Queen. The Queen was known for her wisdom. She agreed to help him.

However, the King overheard them talking. He angrily asked the Queen to leave his palace. The Queen sadly agreed but she requested the King to let her take what she valued most from the palace. The King agreed. The Queen asked him to drink a farewell toast. Now, the drink had a sleeping draught, thus, the King fell asleep. The Queen took him to her tiny hut. When the King awakened, he was very angry. He asked the Queen for an explanation. She told the King, he was dearest to her! The King was ashamed. They returned to the palace, happily.

29. Mother Mary

Once, a poor woodcutter's daughter lived with Mother Mary. The Lady was leaving for a journey and gave the Girl the keys of the thirteen doors of heaven. She forbade her to enter the thirteenth. As soon as she left, the Girl opened the thirteenth door. When Mother Mary came back, the Girl lied and was thrown out from heaven.

The Girl married a King and had many children. The Lady took them away and said, "Your children will come back only when you accept that you opened the forbidden door."

Meanwhile, the Girl was blamed for killing her children. She was being pushed into a burning pyre when she cried out loudly, "Yes, Mother Mary, I did it!" At once, rain fell from the sky and extinguished the flames.

Mother Mary appeared with the children and said, "He who repents his sin and acknowledges it, is forgiven."

30. The Elder-Tree Woman

Once, a little Girl fell sick. She cried, thinking she was missing so many good things in life, being ill. Her mother gave her a cup of tea made from Elder-Tree blossoms.

Suddenly, the blossoms in the teapot turned into a beautiful Woman, dressed in green leaves and white flowers. The Woman told the Girl about an Old Couple who wanted to celebrate their Golden Wedding Anniversary, but had forgotten the date.

Soon the Girl and the Woman were in a beautiful garden with golden flowers. A young man and a pretty woman were getting married there. The Woman said, "This is the Old Couple. Today is their Golden Wedding! They do not remember the date, but they remember the happy times. Good memories are more important than dates!"

When the Girl opened her eyes, she was back in her house! Then on, she was always cheerful.

31. Fitcher Bird

Once, a Wizard kidnapped the eldest sister from a house where three pretty girls lived. However, one day, she disobeyed him and entered a small room, full of dead limbs of humans. The angry Wizard cut her also into pieces.

The second sister also died in the same way. The third sister was very clever. She obeyed the Wizard and he asked her to marry him. However, the Girl secretly put the limbs of her sisters together and brought them back to life.

Then, the Girl packed a huge basket with gold and hid her sisters in it. She asked the Wizard to take the gift to her house. When he went, she covered herself with honey and feathers so she looked like a 'Fitcher Bird' and escaped to her house.

When the Wizard returned, the Girl's brothers followed him. They locked the house from outside and set it on fire!
The evil Wizard died.

1. The Sparrow and Her Children

Once, a Sparrow went off to find food for her four children. When she came back, she found them missing. She was worried, as the children were very young. A few days later, the children came back. The Sparrow asked them how they had managed to live on their own. The eldest son told her that he stayed in a garden and ate caterpillars and other small worms. The second son had lived among the stable boys and fed on grains or corns. The third son had spent the summers on roads and ate the grains of barley. The Sparrow advised them to be careful with all these places, as these places were dangerous. Then, the youngest son told her that he lived in a church and fed on the spiders and flies. The Sparrow happily said, "He who lives in God's shelter is always safe."

2. Little Snow White

Once, there lived a kind King and Queen who had a baby girl. She was extremely fair. Thus, she was named Snow White. When Snow White was very young, her mother died. The King married again, but the new Queen was evil. She had a magical Mirror, which spoke. One day it said, "Snow White is the most beautiful!" So the Queen became jealous of Snow White. She ordered a Hunter to kill Snow White. However, the Hunter left her in the forest and told the Queen that she was dead. Meanwhile, Snow White wandered in the forest, alone and tearful. Fortunately, she found a small cottage. The seven Dwarfs, who were the owners of the cottage, returned after some time. Soon, they became friends and Snow White began living with them.

Then, one day, the evil Queen asked her Mirror who the most beautiful woman was. The Mirror answered, "Snow White is the most beautiful!" Now, the Queen was very angry. She dressed up as an old lady and went to the Dwarf 's cottage when Snow White was alone. There, she gave her a poisoned apple. Snow White ate that apple and fell down, as though dead!

When the Dwarfs returned, they saw Snow White lying lifeless on the ground. They felt very sad and made a glass coffin for her. In her funeral, a young Prince saw the coffin and fell in love with Snow White. He asked his servants to carry the coffin to his palace. However, as the servants were carrying the coffin, the poisoned apple came out of Snow White's mouth and she opened her eyes. The Prince was very happy and asked Snow White to marry him. Snow White then went to live with the Prince in his palace. When the evil Queen heard of this, she died of jealousy!

3. Clever Gretel

Once, there was a clever cook named Gretel. One day, Gretel's Master asked her to prepare two fowls. He was expecting some guests for dinner. The fowls were almost done but the guests had not arrived. The Master said, "I'll go and bring them, personally." Now, Gretel was hungry, so she ate both wings of one fowl and thought, 'If I ate only one wing, the Master would notice something missing.' It was getting late. So Gretel ate the whole fowl. Suddenly her Master arrived. He immediately started sharpening the knife to cut the fowls. The guests, who arrived immediately after, saw him do so. Gretel approached the guests and said quietly, "Run away, my Master plans to cut your ears off!" As the scared guests ran off, Gretel said to her Master, "Oh! The guests ran off with both the fowls." The hungry Master chased his guests, crying out angrily, "Give me at least one!" While he meant one fowl, the guests thought he was asking for their ears!

4. The Golden Goose

Once, an Inn Keeper lived with his two daughters. One day, a traveller came to stay in his inn. He carried a beautiful Goose with golden feathers. The girls wanted to touch the Golden Goose.

After the Traveller slept, the greedy girls crept into his room. They stole the Goose and took it to the market to sell. Just then, the King's men saw them and caught them. They said, "We have been looking for the King's favourite bird and the thief for a long time." The girls were taken to the King's court. The King ordered that they be put in prison. The girls cried out to their Father for help. He said, "If you had not been greedy, you would not have been punished. I cannot help you now!" The King's men took them to prison and they spent the rest of their lives in misery.

5. By the Almshouse Window

One day, an Old Woman looked out of her Almshouse window. She saw poor barefoot Children playing on the road. They had red cheeks and angelic eyes and looked very happy.

The Woman remembered her past. As a child, she had played happily, not bothered by her poverty. When she grew up, she was married in a white frock cut out from an old white dress, stitched by her mother. When she grew older, she had faced many problems. However, she and her husband, who was a dear friend, had supported each other, always. She was young then and had the spirit of youth, which gave her strength. However, eventually, the Woman grew old and her spirit weakened. She had to live in an Almshouse. The Old Woman sadly thought that the little children would also undergo the same life. They would one day stand at the window and relive their past in other children.

6. The Money from Heaven

Once there lived a little Girl who lost her parents and she had no home. She only had some clothes on and some bread. One day, while walking on the road, a poor man begged the Girl for food. She gave him her bread and went ahead. A little ahead she found a boy whose head was cold so she gave him her hat. Then she saw a girl shivering with cold. She pitied the poor girl and covered her with her jacket. Soon she entered a forest and met another girl. As she had no clothes on, the kind Girl gave her own frock to her. As the Girl gave away the last thing she had, lots of money fell from the heaven on her. Magically, there were new clothes on her body.

God had been looking at the kind-hearted little Girl. She became rich and lived happily ever after.

7. The Girl and the frog

Once, there lived an orphan girl, who sat outside the city walls and spun silk. One day, she saw a Frog coming out of a hole in the wall. She quickly spread out a silk handkerchief. Frogs love silk and it is the only thing they creep on. As soon as the Frog saw the handkerchief, he went back into his hole. The Frog soon returned with a small crown and kept it on the handkerchief and went back again. The crown was golden with delicate work. The Girl picked it up and was admiring it, when the Frog returned. He did not see the crown where he had laid it. So he crept up the wall in sorrow, and banged his little head against it till he fell down dead. If the crown were still on the handkerchief, the Frog would have brought more treasures out of the hole.

8. The Rose Garden

Once, a little Girl and a little Boy played together in a rose garden. Sadly, the Boy went missing.

The Girl wondered if he had drowned in the river. Thus, she went to the river and climbed into a boat. Soon, it started drifting down the river. The little Girl was scared and started crying. Then, she saw a small colourful house with a beautiful garden. Just then a Witch, who lived there, came to the riverside. She was a good Witch and so helped the Girl out of the boat. The Witch comforted the Girl and wanted her to stay. She used magic to make the Girl forget her friend and her home, too. However, after a few days, the Girl saw the rose bushes in the Witch's garden, and they reminded her of home. The Girl, at once, ran off to the river. She found her boat and left for home!

9. The Iron Pot

Once, a Princess lost her way while hunting and reached an old cottage. Entering, she saw nothing but a huge Iron Pot. Suddenly, a voice called out from the Pot, "Who are you?"

When the scared Princess explained her plight, the Pot said, "I will help you if you promise to come back and make a hole in my side." The Princess agreed. Magically, the Princess reached home. But now she was afraid to go back into the forest. So, she sent the miller's daughter instead. Try as she might, she was unable to make a hole in the Pot. The Pot told her to go back and send the real Princess. She had to fulfil her promise. It warned her that the Princess would lose her kingdom, otherwise. Finally, the Princess came to old cottage. She scraped and made a huge hole in the Pot. Lo and behold! A handsome Prince came out and the two married and lived happily together.

10. The Wolf and the Fox

Once, a strong Wolf caught a weak Fox. The Wolf growled, "Fox, go get me something to eat or I will eat you!" The Fox fetched a lamb from a farm for the Wolf. The greedy Wolf wanted more and went to get another lamb himself. However, he made too much noise. The farmer heard him and hit him hard. The next day, when the Wolf was hungry, the Fox fetched him pancakes. The greedy Wolf went back for more and got beaten up again. The third time, the Fox took the Wolf to a cellar where meat was kept. The smart Fox did not eat much so that he could escape quickly.

The greedy Wolf, however, ate a lot. The Farmer heard them and came. The Fox had escaped and the Wolf was beaten to death. Through his cleverness, the Fox was finally free of the bossy and greedy Wolf.

11. The Clever Hedgehog

One day, a Hedgehog met a Hare. The Hare made fun of the Hedgehog's legs. The upset Hedgehog challenged him to a race saying, "Don't be so proud of your legs! You will be sorry you made fun of me!" They agreed that the winner would get a gold coin and a bottle of wine.

The Hedgehog's Wife said, "How can you win with your short legs?" He told her to just stand at the finish line and shout "I am here," each time she saw the Hare. The next morning, at the end of every race, the Hare heard the Hedgehog's Wife shout, "I am here." Not knowing the difference between the Hedgehog and his Wife, the Hare asked to race again. He ran and lost the race 273 times and finally, died of exhaustion. The clever Hedgehog thanked his Wife and happily took the gold coin and the wine bottle.

12. The Little Match-Seller

On a snowy New Year's Eve, a poor Girl walked the streets barefoot to sell matches. She was shivering with cold and decided to light the matchsticks to keep herself warm.

The Girl lit a match and imagined herself sitting in a warm room. With the second match, she saw herself eating a splendid dinner. The third time, she was under a beautiful Christmas tree. When she lit another match, she saw her dead grandmother, who loved her a lot. The Girl lit the whole box of matches to keep seeing her grandmother. Then the grandmother picked up the little Girl in her arms and took her to Heaven, where there was no pain or hunger.

The next morning, people found the body of a little Girl with a box of burnt matches. They thought she had tried to warm herself. Nobody knew the beautiful things she saw or the Heaven she entered on New-Year's eve.

13. Rumpelstiltskin

Once, a King asked a miller's daughter to spin straw into gold. An Elf offered to help her but said, "Promise me that you will give me your first-born." The Girl agreed and the Elf spun the gold. The Girl took it to the King. He was very pleased and married her. A year went by and a baby was born to the Girl, now the Queen. Soon after, the Elf appeared and asked for the baby. The Queen pleaded with the Elf. However, he agreed if she could guess his name in three days.

Two days had passed and the Queen was sad. She could not guess the correct name of the Elf. Just then, her maid came and said, "I saw a small man sing that his name was 'Rumpelstiltskin' and that he would soon get the Queen's baby!" The Queen happily went to meet the Elf. She told him that his name was Rumpelstiltskin. This enraged the Elf so much that he went away stomping, never to come back again!

14. The Lost Friend

Once, a Young Girl was searching for her lost friend. She met a Crow who said, "I think I know where to find your friend. My sweetheart lives in the Princess's palace. She informs me about all that happens there." The Crow then went on to tell her how the Princess wanted to marry a person who was not just handsome but smart as well. Many boys turned up, but everyone forgot how to speak when they came before her. One fine day, a Young Boy came to the palace, without a carriage. His eyes sparkled and had beautiful long hair, but had poor clothes. He answered all the questions asked by the Princess. So, she decided to marry him. The Young Girl was sure it was her friend and wanted to meet him. The Crow led her to the palace. However, the Young Boy was not her friend. The Prince and Princess were very kind to the Girl. They presented her with a carriage and horse to help in her search.

15. The Robber-Girl

The Girl went further looking for her friend. She rode the carriage through a dense forest. Suddenly, some robbers stopped the carriage. They thought a Princess was riding the golden carriage. Along with the robbers came a Girl. She was as old as the Young Girl in the carriage, but was stronger and darker. She jumped onto the carriage. Then the two rode to the robbers' house. The house was dark, dirty and full of animals. The Young Girl was very scared. That night, the two girls had some soup and lay on the straw. The Young Girl told the Robber Girl her story. The Robber Girl's Pigeons had seen the Snow Queen take the Young Boy with her. The Reindeer knew where the Snow Queen lived. Thus, in the morning, the Robber Girl sent her Reindeer to carry the Young Girl to her friend in the North Pole.

16. The Finland Woman

The Young Girl was on her way to the North Pole, in search of her friend. She had reached Finland riding on the back of a Reindeer. There, they met an Old Lady who lived in a hut under the ground. It was very hot in the hut. The Young Girl had to take off her woollens. The Old Lady gave the Reindeer the directions to reach the Snow Queen's palace and said, "My child, your friend is very happy with the Snow Queen. Unless the pieces of the magic mirror are removed from his eyes and heart, he will not return." Then the Young Girl and the Reindeer left. Their woollens were left behind, so they felt very cold. The Reindeer dropped off the Girl in the palace garden and returned. The Young Girl was scared. Thus, she prayed and prayed. And Angels with spears and shields came down to help her.

17. The Palace of the Snow Queen

Far away on the North Pole was the Palace of the Snow Queen. The Young Girl had reached here, searching for her best friend. The Palace was empty and the walls were made of snow. The northern lights were the only ones to be seen there. In the centre of the Palace was a lake, where the Snow Queen sat.

Then, in a corner, the Young Girl saw the Young Boy. He was blue and sat still, as if frozen. She ran and hugged him. However, he did not recognise her. Her warm tears fell on his ice heart and it melted. The Little Boy started crying. His tears washed away the mirror pieces from his eyes. Then he recognised her. They walked hand-in-hand and met two Reindeers outside the Palace. The Reindeers carried them as far as the outskirts of their town. From there, they ran home, together.

18. The Wilful Child

Once, there was a Little Girl who was very willful. She had a mind of her own and would always do what she wanted and not what her Mother wished. Her Mother found it very difficult to cope with her unruly behaviour. One day, the Girl did not listen to her Mother and went to play on the riverside. While she played, she fell in the river and drowned. The Mother was heartbroken on her daughter's death. The Little Girl was placed in a coffin and lowered into her grave. Just then, her arms came out. No amount of earth was able to keep the arms down. The crying Mother then peeped into the coffin. As her tears touched the Girl's face, suddenly, her eyes opened and she came back to life! The Mother pulled her out of the coffin. The Little Girl hugged her Mother and promised that she would never be naughty again!

19. The Six Swans

Once, a King married a lady, who was evil. Thus, the King hid his six sons and only daughter from her. But the wicked Stepmother found the Princes and turned them into Swans through her magic. To help them, their sister had to remain mute for six years and sew a shirt for each. The Princess started to sew. Soon, she was married to a Prince. However, she still had to be mute. The Prince's wicked mother would use her silence and accuse her of being a man-eater. Finally the Prince got so angry that he ordered her death. On the day the Princess was to be executed, her brothers came in the form of Swans. By this time, all the shirts were done. The Swans wore the shirts and turned back into their human forms. They at once told the Prince the truth about their sister. The princess could also talk now! The Prince apologised to the Princess. Then on, they all lived happily ever after.

20. The Hen and the Cock

Once, a Hen and a Cock were friends. They both went to a hill to collect nuts. They decided to share the nuts they found. Soon, the Hen found a large nut. However, the selfish Hen ate it herself. The nut was so big that she choked on it. She shouted to the Cock to get her some water.

The Cock ran to the Stream; but the Stream demanded some silk from a Bride. The Bride demanded a wreath from a tree. After fetching the Bride and Stream what they wanted, he went back to the Hen with water. Sadly, the Hen had already died! The Cock took her in a carriage to bury her. However, on reaching the stream, he could not get across. Then, a Stone offered to help. The Cock finally crossed the river with the help of the Stone, and buried the Hen. He sat there mourning her death. Finally, the Cock died too.

21. The Magical Cabbages

Once, there was a Hunter. He possessed a Wishing Cloak and a Magic Necklace, which gave him a gold coin every day. He took them to set out to explore distant lands. One night, he took shelter in a Witch's castle. Now, the Witch had also trapped a young Maiden there.

The greedy Witch put the Hunter in a deep sleep and stole his things. Then, she left him in a far off land. When the Hunter awoke, he knew he had been tricked. Angrily, he started walking until he came across a cabbage patch. He ate one and immediately changed into a donkey! Then, he ate another and changed back to himself! He gathered the Magical Cabbages and returned to the castle. He then tricked the Witch into eating the Cabbage. She turned into a donkey! Then, wearing his Wishing Cloak and his Magic Necklace, he returned home with the Maiden.

22. The Mean Stepmother

Once, there was a pretty Girl who had an unkind Stepmother and a mean Sister but a loving Brother. Now, the Brother had made a painting of the Girl. One day, the King happened to see the painting and wanted to make the Girl his bride. The Brother told the Girl to wear her golden dress and get ready to wed the King. Now, the wicked Stepmother did not like this, so she put a spell on the Girl. So, the Girl appeared ugly and the Sister appeared pretty. Thus, both the Brother and the King got fooled. The King married the wicked Sister. But the magic spell would last only for a short while! As time passed, the Stepmother forgot to bewitch the sisters again. The magic spell started to wear off! One day, the King noticed the change and realised that he had been fooled! He imprisoned the Stepmother and the Sister until they told him the truth. Finally, he married the Girl and they lived happily.

23. The White Dove

Once, there was young Girl who got lost in a forest, while picking flowers. Unknowingly, she went deeper into the forest and could not find her way out. Tired, she sat under a Tree and wept.

Suddenly, a White Dove flew down and dropped a Key on her lap. To her astonishment, it spoke! It guided her to a tiny Lock on the Tree. She opened it and found a room where she could eat and rest. Then the Dove flew away. Next day, the White Dove came back and asked the Girl for help. The Girl readily agreed. The White Dove led her to a Witch's cottage and told her to fetch a ring from there, without her knowledge. The fearless Girl got the ring and suddenly the cottage turned into a palace and the Dove into a Prince! She had broken the Witch's spell. The Prince and the Girl married, and lived happily ever after.

24. The Hungry Chickens

A Farmer and his Wife kept several Chickens. These Chickens had many little chicks. Most of the time, they all went hungry. One day, the Farmer was working in his fields and his Wife had gone out. There were lots of crumbs on the dining table. One Chicken poked in her head and said, "Let's eat these delicious crumbs." "No," said another Chicken, "we will be beaten!"

"No one's here. Let's go. At least we won't be hungry," urged the first Chicken.

All the Chickens flocked on the dining table. They pecked away and the chicks ate what fell off the table! So many Chickens pecking away on a wooden table made a lot of noise!

The Farmer came running, with a big stick. His Wife also returned. They both started beating up the Chickens. As they ran, one Chicken said to the others, "See, I warned you! We got beaten and we're still hungry!"

25. The Fox and the Cat

Once, a Cat met a Fox in the forest. The Cat had heard that the Fox was very clever and full of experience. Thus, she greeted the Fox and asked, "Sir, how are you?" The Fox was very arrogant. He said, "Why should I reply? You are not worthy enough to talk to me! Tell me, what arts do you know?" The Cat replied, "I know only one art, that is, the art of climbing a tree to escape from Hounds." The Fox laughed at her and said, "Oh! I know plenty of arts and I am clever. Let me show you how to escape from Hounds like a human."

Just then, a Hunter came with four Hounds. The Cat immediately rushed up a tree. However, the Hounds caught the Fox. "Alas!" said the Cat, "Too bad your knowledge of the various arts could not help you!"

26. A Good Bargain

Once, a foolish Peasant had seven coins. He then heard the Frogs croak, "Aik!" The Peasant thought they croaked "Eight". He gave the seven coins to the Frogs to count. However, never got them back! Similarly, he gave away beef to the Dogs, thinking they'd give it to the Butcher for some money. Alas! The Dogs ate up the beef! The Peasant narrated his losses to the King to seek justice. The King's daughter laughed aloud! The King offered her in marriage but the Peasant denied. The angry King said, "Come back and take five hundred." The King meant five hundred 'blows' but the Peasant understood 'coins'! Two men had threatened the Peasant to repay his loans, with the King's reward! When it was time for the five hundred 'blows', the Peasant said, "I would like to divide my reward between these two men." The King was impressed and offered the Peasant a lot of gold and made him a minister in his court.

27. The Wolf and the Seven Little Kids

Once, a Mother Goat left her seven little Kids at home. A cunning Wolf wanted to eat the Kids. He ate a lot of chalk that made his voice soft. He applied white paint on his body. Then he called out, "Dear Babies! Open the door!"

The Kids heard the soft voice and saw the white paws. Thinking it was their Mother, they opened the door. The Wolf swallowed all the Kids. The Mother Goat returned and found her Kids missing. She saw the Wolf asleep. His stomach wobbled. She understood that her Kids were inside. She cut open the Wolf 's stomach and the Kids happily jumped out.

The Mother Goat then put seven stones in the Wolf 's stomach and sewed it up. When he awoke, the Wolf found his stomach to be heavy, because of the stones. When he bent to drink water from the well, he fell inside and drowned, because of his heavy weight.

28. Jorinda and Joringel

Once, an old Witch lived in a castle in a forest. Now, if a pretty maiden wandered close to her castle, the Witch would turn her into a bird. She kept all the birds in a cage. The Witch turned young boys into statues and left them outside her castle. Their spell wore off after some time, and they went back. Jorinda and Joringel were engaged. One day, they wandered too close to the castle. Jorinda became a nightingale and Joringel a statue! The Witch appeared, put Jorinda in a cage and took her away. When Joringel came alive, he was very sad. He looked for ways to free Jorinda. Then, suddenly, he found a blood red flower with a pearl in its centre. He took this flower to the castle. Once there, Joringel touched the Witch with the flower, which took away all her magical powers. He also used the flower to turn Jorinda back to a human along with all the other captured maidens. Jorinda and Joringel lived happily ever after.

1. King Thrushbeard

A proud Princess rejected all her suitors. She especially made fun of a Prince by calling him "Thrushbeard."

Her father was very angry and married her to a Beggar. The Beggar took the Princess across many places that belonged to King Thrushbeard. The Beggar asked the Princess to work for a living, but she failed at everything!

One day, while the Princess was selling pots, a horseman destroyed them. So, her husband got her a job as a maid in the King's palace.

Now, a feast was being arranged at the palace to celebrate the marriage of the King's son. The Princess secretly peeped through the curtains to look at the preparations. Suddenly, Thrushbeard pulled her into the party. Then, he told her that he had dressed as a Beggar for her love, and wanted her to lose her pride.

The Princess was very happy and they lived blissfully thereafter.

2. Rapunzel

Once, there lived a couple who did not have any children.

One day, the Wife looked out of her window and thought, "Ah! What a beautiful Rampion flower. But it is in the garden of the evil Witch. I could never go there!" She said to her husband, "Oh dear, how I want that Rampion!"

The Husband loved her and went to fetch the flower. However, the Witch saw him in her garden. The scared Husband said, "My Wife wants this flower very much."

The evil Witch said, "You can take the Rampion if you promise to give me your child, when it is born." The poor Husband agreed.

A few years later, a girl was born to the couple. The Witch took away the baby and named her Rapunzel. She locked Rapunzel in a room on the top of a tower. The room had only one small window.

Rapunzel grew up into a beautiful young girl with very long hair. However, the evil Witch still kept her locked in the tower at all times.

One such day, a young Prince was passing by the tower and saw Rapunzel looking out of her window. Amazed at her beauty, he called to Rapunzel, "O pretty lady, I have fallen in love with you. Let your hair down the window. I shall climb up this tower on your braid and rescue you from the evil Witch!" Rapunzel let down her long braid.

However, the Witch saw the Prince in Rapunzel's room. She screamed, "Rapunzel! I will cut your hair and turn you into a frog!"

To this, the Prince said angrily, "You shall not harm my future wife!" and killed the evil Witch with his mighty sword. Thus, Rapunzel was free.

Soon, the Prince and Rapunzel were married and spent their lives happily together.

3. The Magic Apple Tree

Violet and her two elder Sisters lived with their Mother in a village. They were all gifted witches, except for Violet. Thus, they were all cruel to her.

One day, Violet was weeping, when suddenly, the Witch Queen appeared and gave her a magic seed to plant in the backyard. Violet planted it at once.

The next morning, there stood a silver Tree with golden apples. The Mother and Sisters tried their best to pluck the apples but could not do so. Finally, they allowed Violet to try. She easily plucked them. Alas! The Sisters grew more jealous.

One day, a handsome Knight was passing by. He asked for an apple and in return, he would fulfil one wish of the giver. Violet plucked an apple and presented it to the Knight. According to her wish, they married. Surprisingly, the Magic Apple Tree appeared at their garden the next day!

The hungry Master chased his guests, crying out angrily, "Give me at least one!" While he meant one fowl, the guests thought he was asking for their ears!

4. Man and Woman

Once, a Man wanted to marry a Woman. Now, this Woman had a Father, a Mother, a Sister and a Brother. Thus, the Man went to ask the Father's permission to marry the Woman. The Father agreed, on the condition that the Mother, the Brother, the Sister and the Woman should agree.

Thus, he then went to the Mother. She agreed, on the condition that the Father, the Brother, the Sister and the Woman should agree.

Next, he went to the Brother. He agreed, on the condition that the Father, the Mother, the Sister and the Woman should agree.

Then, he went to the Sister. She agreed, on the condition that the Father, the Mother, the Brother and the Woman should agree.

Finally, the Man went to the Woman, who agreed! Thus, the Man married the Woman and the Father, the Mother, the Brother and the Sister, all agreed.

5. Allerleira

Once, a beautiful princess, Allerleira, ran from her father's palace to escape being married to an old king.

She went and lived in the forest. Then, she changed into ordinary clothes and covered her face with soot.

One day, a Prince saw Allerleira in the forest and felt pity for her. He took her to his palace. She started working there as a cook and led a miserable life.

A few days later, a festival was organised in the palace. Allerleira wanted to see the festival. Thus, she washed her face and wore a silk gown. She looked like a princess again.

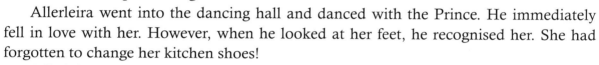

Allerleira went into the dancing hall and danced with the Prince. He immediately fell in love with her. However, when he looked at her feet, he recognised her. She had forgotten to change her kitchen shoes!

Allerleira told him the truth. The Prince forgave her and they were married soon.

6. Sweetheart Roland

A young Girl lived with her mother, who was a cruel witch.

One day, her sweetheart Roland, helped her escape the clutches of the witch. Using the witch's magic wand, they turned into a fiddler and a flower. Then they played a tune, which killed the witch.

Then, Roland went home to prepare for their wedding. Once there, another witch enchanted him and he forgot the Girl.

Meanwhile, the Girl was still a flower. A Shepherd plucked her and took her home. After this, the Shepherd noticed that his house was magically cared for! Then, after some time, the Girl came back to her real form. The Shepherd wanted to marry her, but she was true to her sweetheart, and hence, refused.

Just then, the Girl heard of Roland's marriage. She went to his wedding and sang, thus, waking him from his spell.

Roland was happy to see his sweetheart. They both were married and lived happily thereafter.

7. Fredrick and Catherine

Once, a man called Fredrick and his wife, Catherine, lived in a village.

One day, before Fredrick went to work in the fields, he told Catherine to have lunch ready by the time he returned. However, Catherine was careless in the kitchen and did not prepare any food. When she just served empty plates before Fredrick, he was very angry.

The next day, when Fredrick was out at work, some thieves stole all the coins he had buried in the backyard. This angered Fredrick more.

Then, one day, when Catherine was working in the fields, she fell asleep and cut up her clothes instead of the corn. She was so horrified that she went in her torn clothes to the neighbouring turnip patch and stole some turnips.

The owner saw her and thought her to be the devil. He, at once, ran away in fear, never to come back. So, Catherine and Fredrick took over the neighbouring fields, and became rich. And now, Fredrick was not angry any more!

8. The Hare's Bride

Once, a beautiful Girl lived with her Mother. One day, she went to her garden and met a Hare.

He said, "Sit on my tail. I will take you to a beautiful world."

The Hare took the Girl to his burrow, which was deep under the earth. The Girl was frightened and wanted to go home.

However, the Hare laughed wickedly and said, "I will marry you and keep you here forever."

The Girl started crying but the Hare told her to get ready and went out to call the guests for the wedding.

After some time, the Girl's Mother came to look for her in the garden. She heard her daughter's cry at a distance and dug the earth. She pulled out the Girl from the Hare's burrow and took her home.

Then, the Mother hugged her and said, "You should never go anywhere without telling your parents." The Girl agreed and apologised.

9. Mother Holle

Once, there was a hard-working Girl, who had a lazy Stepsister.

One day, the Girl dropped a bucket in the well by mistake. Suddenly, a beautiful woman in a blue dress appeared. She said, "Do not cry, dear one! I am Mother Holle. If you collect the golden apples from your garden for me, I shall give you your bucket!"

The Girl worked hard and collected all the golden apples in a basket. Mother Holle gave her a gold bucket in return.

Now, the Stepsister was watching all this. She, too, went to the well and dropped a bucket in it. Mother Holle appeared and asked her also to collect golden apples.

The lazy Stepsister gave her two apples that had fallen on the ground. Mother Holle then gave her a gold bucket. But, it stuck to her hands and would not come off. Thus, the Stepsister was punished for being lazy.

10. The Riddle

Once, a Prince wanted to marry a beautiful Princess. The Princess said, "Ask me a riddle. I shall marry you if I cannot answer it."

Thus, the Prince asked her, "One killed none, yet killed twelve. What is it?"

The Princess thought hard for some time. Yet, she could not find the answer. After three days, she said, "I give up, Prince. I shall marry you. Pray tell me the answer first!"

The Prince said, "Once, a wicked witch poisoned my horse. A raven ate that dead horse. I killed the raven and took it with me. On my way home, I met twelve bandits. I gave them the raven to eat. All twelve bandits died after eating it, for the raven had the horse's poison in his blood. Thus, the raven killed none, but killed twelve."

Thus, the clever Prince married the Princess. They both lived happily together.

11. The Red Shoes

Once, there lived a poor orphan Girl. She had no shoes. The shoemaker's kind wife stitched a clumsy pair of Red Shoes for her. The Girl loved them.

Soon, an old lady adopted the Girl. The lady took good care of the Girl, but burnt her Red Shoes. Then, the Girl had to go to school. She went and bought Red Shoes to wear to her school. Everyone made fun of her shoes. The Old Lady was annoyed and banned her from wearing them again.

One day, the Girl secretly wore the Red Shoes. Now, these Red Shoes were actually magical dancing shoes. They kept dancing all over the town and forest for many days and nights. Poor Girl – she could not stop dancing nor remove the shoes!

Finally, the Girl danced her way into a river. There the Red Shoes slipped off from her tired feet. The Girl sat on the riverbank, promising to never wear any kind of Red Shoes ever again!

12. Grandmother

Once an old, wrinkled Grandmother had a hymnbook in which she kept an old withered rose. She would often look at it and smile. Then, tears would come into her eyes.

Grandmother had got that rose many years ago from her husband, when she was very young. She kept that rose because it reminded her of that day and also of her loving husband, who was no more.

One day, after Grandmother had finished telling a long story to her grandchildren, she leaned in her arm-chair to sleep awhile. She smiled in her sleep and then passed away, peacefully. Grandmother was buried in a black coffin with the hymn-book under her head, as she had wished.

On her grave, people planted a rose-tree. From the church nearby, hymns would be played, which were also written in Grandmother's hymn-book.

And Grandmother is still remembered through the roses and the hymns.

13. The Darning Needle

Once, there was a Darning Needle who thought itself to be very delicate.

One day, the Cook broke the Needle while sewing, and it became like a Pin. The Cook kept it in a handkerchief but the Needle was proud and thought it deserved a better place. Thus, it jumped into the sink and floated away on a journey with the dirty water.

However, the Needle became lost in the gutter for a long time. Yet, it criticised everything in the gutter. After many days, a few boys found the broken Needle. It looked so black and dirty, they thought it was a Nail and stuck it in an eggshell and let it float.

The Needle still kept talking about how fine and slim it looked on the shell. The vain Needle said that though it was delicate, it was strong and had tolerated a lot of things in life. Finally, a wagon passed over the shell, crushing the Needle completely…

14. The Flax

Once there was a beautiful Flax plant who was very happy. One day, a Fern sang to the Flax mournfully, "The song has ended."

The Flax however said, "The best is yet to come."

Then the Flax was painfully pulled out, broken and made into White Linen and taken to a clergyman's wife. The Linen forgot all its pain and was very happy by the attention it got.

When the Linen turned to rags, it was converted into Paper by another painful process. The Paper thought happily, that now it would travel the world. It was made into a beautiful Book for many people to read.

When it was old, the Book was burnt in a fireplace. Its Ashes rose high up, higher than the Flax plant could raise itself, and the Ash thought, "The song is never over. The best is yet to come."

15. Brother and Sister

Once, a Brother and his Sister escaped into the forest fearing their stepmother, a Witch. However, the Witch cast a spell on the water streams in the forest. When the Brother collected some drinking water, he turned into a Deer. The Sister was deeply saddened. She tied her gold chain around his neck.

Then, a King came hunting into the forest. He saw the Deer with the gold chain. He followed and reached where the Deer lived. The King fell in love with the Deer's Sister and married her.

Now, the Witch and her daughter were jealous of the new Queen. They tried to kill her by locking her in a dark room. The Deer helped his Sister escape. They told the King about the Witch's wickedness. The King ordered the Witch to be put in hot oil. The moment the Witch died, the Deer turned back into the Queen's Brother!

16. The Four Servants

Once there was a Sorceress who had a beautiful Daughter. She had set three dangerous tasks for anyone who wanted to marry her Daughter. No suitor succeeded, rather all died while trying.

Now, there was a Prince who had four skilled Servants, a fat one, a very tall one, one who could hear everything and one who was very strong. He set off with them to meet the Sorceress and marry her Daughter.

The Sorceress gave him the three tasks. First, he had to find a lost ring; second, he had to eat food meant for a hundred people; and finally, defeat a dragon.

The Prince told the Hear-All Servant to locate the ring. It was on top of a mountain. The Tall Servant brought it. The Fat Servant ate up all the food and the Strong Servant defeated the dragon.

Thus, the Prince was happily married to the Sorceress' Daughter.

17. The Hen that Laid the Golden Egg

One day, a Farmer found a golden egg in his hen house. He happily showed it to his Wife.

The next day, the Farmer's Wife caught the Hen that laid the golden egg. She rushed to the Farmer with the Hen and said, "We'll never have to work again!"

The Farmer built a special coop for the Hen and kept her separate from the others. Every morning, the Hen laid a golden egg and the Farmer grew rich.

However, as their money increased, they also grew greedier. They were not satisfied with one golden egg a day.

"If we could get all the golden eggs together from the Hen, we could get richer faster," the Farmer's Wife said. "The gold must be hidden inside the Hen."

The Farmer and his Wife killed the Hen to take out the gold. However, they found no gold inside and the Hen was dead!

18. The Father and His Two Daughters

There lived a Man in the countryside. He had two daughters. One daughter was married to a gardener and the other was married to a tile-maker. They both lived in different towns.

One day, the Man visited his Daughter, who was the gardener's wife. He asked her, "My daughter, how are you? Is there anything you wish for?"

She replied that she just wished that there would be heavy rains, so that her plants may be well watered.

Then the Man left to visit his other Daughter, who was the tile-maker's wife. He asked her the same question. She said she wished that there would be no rainfall and sun would shine hot and bright, so that the tiles would all dry well.

When the Man heard both his Daughters' wishes, he realised that they both were happy in their own world, even if they had very different needs.

19. The Miser and his Gold

Once, there was a rich Farmer, who had a large farm. However, he was a miser.

One day, the Miser bought a brick of gold from the goldsmith. He was worried that someone might steal his treasure. Thus, he buried his gold underneath a tree.

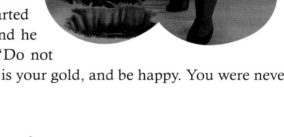

The Miser then visited the tree every day to check on his gold. Once, a clever servant followed the Miser.

Then, one night, the servant went to the tree. He dug around it and found the gold. He quickly ran away with it.

The next day, the Miser went to the tree and saw that his gold had been stolen. He started crying loudly. His wife came out running and he told her about the missing gold. She said, "Do not cry! Now bury a stone near the tree. Think it is your gold, and be happy. You were never going to use the gold anyway!"

20. The Happy Family

Once there was an old estate where no one lived. Burdocks covered the estate garden. Burdock leaves were used in ancient times to breed Great White Snails, which were made into delicious stews and eaten by the royal family.

Now, the last two surviving White Snails lived in the garden. They were left, because nobody lived in the estate any more. The White Snail couple did not have any children of their own, so they adopted a little Common Snail and brought it up. The couple loved their adopted son. They got him married to another Common Snail and left the whole garden to the young couple when they died.

The young couple had numerous children. They all lived in the garden as a happy family.

21. The Girl Without Hands

Once, the Devil said to a poor Man, "If you cut your Daughter's hands, I shall give you gold." The greedy Man cut his Daughter's hands, at once.

However, the sad Girl left home and set out for the city.

In the city, the Girl came across a beautiful garden. Many trees with delicious fruits stood around a pond in that garden. The Girl was tired and hungry. As she sat under a tree, an Angel dropped its fruits into her mouth! Suddenly, a Man appeared. He said, "Who is eating the fruits of my garden?"

The scared Girl said, "My father cut my hands, so I left his house. I ate your fruits because I was hungry. I am sorry."

The Man saw that the Girl was very beautiful. He said, "O beautiful lady, I am the King of this city. Please marry me!"

The Girl agreed and the King gave her silver arms. Soon, they were married.

22. The Seven Ravens

Once, a Girl fell very sick. Her Parents asked her seven brothers to fetch water for her. However, all the lakes were dry. The brothers could not find any water anywhere.

Meanwhile, the Parents thought that the Boys had forgotten to bring water. They cursed them, saying, "The lazy Boys shall turn into Ravens and have no family!"

When the Girl was well, she felt very sad for her dear brothers. She set out to find them.

Soon, she saw the seven Ravens. She said, "O Ravens! I know you are my brothers. Come home with me!"

To this, the Ravens said, "Our Parents did not have faith in us. Make a sheet of thorns to prove that you love us!"

Thus, the loving Girl began knitting a sheet of thorns. Her hands bled. When the Ravens saw this, they came close to her. Lo! They became humans again, for they now had their family back.

23. The Rosebush and the Sparrows

Once, there was a beautiful Rosebush that covered the wall of a farmhouse. Close to it lived a family of Sparrows in their nest.

One day, the Mother-Sparrow was caught by some boys, who painted her with golden paint. While flying back, other birds followed her and pecked at her, thinking she was a strange creature. The Mother-Sparrow fell down and died in the Rosebush.

Some days later, the farmhouse caught fire. Everything was burnt except the Rosebush. The Sparrow's children, however, managed to escape. A painter saw this scene and sketched the burnt farmhouse. He took away the Rosebush with him.

The Sparrow's children grew up and went to different places. The eldest Sparrow went to Copenhagen. There, she met her family of sparrows and also saw the neighbouring Rosebush planted over the grave of Thorvaldsen, a famous Danish sculptor. The painter had gifted the Rosebush to the sculptor. Thorvaldsen had desired his grave to be covered by it! The old neighbours met again!

24. The Old House

Once, there was a very Old House, where an Old Man stayed. Across the street lived a small Boy. The Boy and the Man would look at each other from their windows. One day, the Boy packed a small Tin Soldier and gifted it to the Old Man, for he was lonely.

In return, the Old Man invited the Boy to join him. When he went over, the Soldier asked the Boy to take him back, for he was bored in the Old House. When the Boy refused, the Soldier jumped down and fell between the holes in the floor of the House.

After many years, when the Boy grew up and got married, he returned to the place where the Old House had stood years ago.

One day, his wife found a Tin Soldier while planting a flower. Her husband then told her the story of the Old Man in the Old House.

25. The Angel

Every time, a good Child dies, an Angel takes the dead child to all its favourite places. They both also take some flowers to heaven, where the flowers can bloom better.

In heaven, God kisses the flowers and gives them a voice to sing.

While carrying one such Child, the Angel stopped at a cluttered street, where a broken flowerpot lay. They took the pot with them and the Angel told the Child the story behind the pot.

Once, there was a sickly little Boy who could barely walk. He had never seen the trees outside. One day, the neighbour's Son brought him a flower with the roots still attached. The little Boy used to pretend it was a tree and he took very good care of it till he died.

"But how do you know this?" asked the Child. "I was that sickly little Boy," smiled the Angel.

26. The Useful Cat

Once, a wise Old Man lived with his Son. Before dying, he said, "Son, I don't have anything to give you except my Cat. But, I assure you that you can make money if you use it wisely." The Son did not know what to do with the Cat and decided to sell it.

He travelled from one village to another, but could not find a buyer. Finally, he reached the King's palace.

The King was sitting unhappily in the garden. The Son asked him, "Why are you upset?"

He replied, "A naughty rat entered my room and is creating havoc. All the servants have failed to catch him."

The Son left his Cat in the King's room. The Cat caught the rat and killed it.

The King was very pleased and kept the Son and his Cat in the palace. The Son spent the rest of his life in great comfort.

27. The Hidden Money

Once, a Family was having dinner with their Guest. Suddenly, the Guest saw a Child, dressed in white enter the house. The Child silently went into the next room and soon left the house.

The same incident occurred the next day. The Guest enquired the family about the Child. Surprisingly, no one in the Family had noticed him. The third day, the Guest followed the Child and saw him digging the floor.

The Guest at once told the Family what he saw. They searched under the floor and found some money. The Family realised that it was their Child who had died a month ago. They had once given him that money to give to the poor. He had buried it under the floor for himself and his soul was now restless.

The parents took the money and gave it to the poor and the Child was never seen again.

28. The Water-Nix

Once, there was a Brother and a Sister with magical powers. Their Parents warned them, "Your powers will go away if you're wet."

Once, they were playing by a well that belonged to an evil Water-Nix. The Water-Nix caught them and put them inside the well. She made them work very hard. The children were tired and wet, and had no magical powers left.

As soon as they dried, their magical powers returned. They held the well rope and climbed out.

The Water-Nix chased them in anger. The Sister threw a thistle that grew into big, thorny bushes. The Water-Nix climbed over them.

The Brother threw a comb. It became a high wall with sharp teeth, which the Water-Nix also cleared.

The Sister threw her mirror that turned into a hall of mirrors. The Water-Nix went home to fetch an axe to break the mirrors.

Meanwhile, the children ran home safely.

29. A Rose from Homer's Grave

A lot of stories talk about the love of the Nightingale for the Rose. There grew a beautiful Rose on a hedge. The Nightingale sang of his troubles to her, but the Rose did not care.

Now, this Rose grew on the grave of the great poet, Homer. She thought she would only bloom to honour such a great man and was too valuable to bloom for a Nightingale.

One day, the Rose dreamt that a man from a distant land plucked her and put her in a book. He then took her back to his homeland.

When the Rose woke up, she bloomed more beautiful than ever. But to her alarm, just like in her dream, the man from the distant land plucked her and put her in a book. He took her back to his country.

All she was remembered now was as a Rose from Homer's Grave!

30. Good Luck Can Lie in a Pin

Once, there lived a poor Man. He worked hard to make umbrella handles and rings. In his garden, was a Pear Tree that never bore any fruits. He thought he was very unlucky.

One day, there was a great storm. A branch broke from the Pear Tree. The Man made wooden pears of different sizes for his children from it. While working, the Man saw that that button on an umbrella was spoilt. He could not find a small button. Then, he saw the smallest pear that he had made, lying on the floor. Making a hole in it, he put a string through it and fastened it to the umbrella.

Surprisingly, the pear button worked well. Then on, he began making pear buttons for the umbrellas. Many people asked the Man for these special buttons. Soon, he became a rich man.

The Man realised that good luck comes through hard work and not things!

31. The Fir Tree

There was once a pretty little Fir Tree. It looked around and saw that the other Pine trees were very tall! The Fir Tree wanted to be taller than them.

Two winters passed and now, the Fir Tree was tall. When the Woodcutters came to cut down all the old trees, the Fir Tree was scared. The Tree was also curious to know what would become of the cut wood.

Then one day, the Fir Tree was cut and taken into a beautiful apartment. It was decorated with many pretty things. The children danced around it, before opening their presents. A jolly old man then told them the story of the Christ Child. It was the happiest evening in the Tree's life. After that day, the Tree was cut up and used as firewood. While burning in the fire, the Tree died, remembering all the happy times it had in the forest!

1. The Ugly Duckling

In the countryside, a Mother Duck sat on her nest containing five eggs. Finally, there was a Crack! Little ducklings came out of the eggs, except for one. A little gray creature came out of that egg. It was ugly and large.

The Mother Duck took her children to meet the other ducks. When they saw the Ugly Duckling, everyone made fun of him. Tired of being teased and made fun of, he went to a moor where they treated him worse. Everywhere he went, he was treated badly because he was ugly. Autumn and winter passed away like this.

Finally, in spring, he was swimming in the water. Miserably, he saw his reflection. He was not ugly any more! He was a graceful, beautiful swan now! He swam around with the other swans while children threw cake and bread to him. He never called anyone ugly, because he knew all creatures were beautiful.

2. Cinderella

Once, a woman died of illness, leaving behind her husband and daughter.

Soon, the man married again. His new wife had two daughters. His own daughter was very sad now, for her Stepmother and Stepsisters were cruel. They made her do all the housework and asked her to sleep by the fire. Every morning, she would wake up with cinders from the fire. Thus, they named her Cinderella.

One day, the Prince of that kingdom invited everyone to a ball, where he would choose his future wife.

The Stepsisters stitched pretty dresses for the ball. Cinderella also wanted to go. Her Stepmother said, "You dirty wretch! There is so much work yet to be done. You cannot go!"

Thus, on the evening of the ball, Cinderella wept, left all alone. Suddenly, a fairy appeared. She gave Cinderella a beautiful gown and silver shoes. Now Cinderella was ready for the ball! But the fairy told her that the magic would end at the stroke of midnight – she would have to return before that.

At the ball, the Prince fell in love with beautiful Cinderella. He would dance only with her. Suddenly the clock started chiming. It was midnight! Cinderella was frightened, and she ran towards her house, but lost a shoe at the palace.

The Prince found her shoe and called his men. He said, "Every girl in the kingdom will try on the slipper. It will only fit the girl I love."

Thus, his men set out. Soon, they reached Cinderella's house. Both Stepsisters tried the shoe but their feet did not fit.

Suddenly, one of the Prince's men saw Cinderella behind the curtain. He said, "Please come and try the shoe."

The Stepsisters laughed, as they thought that it could never fit Cinderella. However, Cinderella's foot slipped into the shoe easily. It was a perfect fit!

Soon, the Prince married Cinderella and they lived happily ever after.

3. Grandpa's Play

Once, little Anna and her Grandpa were alone at home. Grandpa decided that they would perform a play in the Nursery. Since they were only two people, Grandpa thought that they would use a Glove, Pipe-head, Waistcoat and Boots as actors. The Pipe-head was the father, the Glove was the daughter, the Waistcoat was the lover and the Boot was a suitor.

Little Anna became the audience. She requested Grandpa to speak the actor's dialogues in verses, just like grown up actors. Grandpa gladly agreed!

In the play, the Pipe-head wanted his daughter, the Glove, to marry the Boot. However, she loved the Waistcoat. The Pipe-head did not agree to marry his daughter to the Waistcoat. Then, the Waistcoat put him in its pocket! The poor Pipe-head had to agree now! The Glove and the Waistcoat were married.

Thus, the play ended and Little Anna and Grandpa went for tea.

4. Amelia and Jack

Once, there was a little girl called Amelia. Little Amelia lived with her Aunt Molly and loved playing with dolls.

Amelia had two naughty Brothers who took lessons from a young boy called Jack. They teased her for playing with dolls. But, Jack was a kind boy and was nice to Amelia. He even taught her a song about dolls. Even Aunt Molly thought that Jack was being silly, but Little Amelia enjoyed talking to Jack.

Many years passed. Amelia was a beautiful girl and Jack, a handsome boy now. They still spent a lot of time together. They collected flowers and sang songs. Wise Aunt Molly now loved Jack as she loved Amelia. She did not think he was being silly any more, for she knew that Jack and Amelia were in love. She bought two beautiful silver rings. Jack and Amelia exchanged the rings and were soon happily married.

5. Belle's Mistake

Belle was a rich, spoilt girl. She went to a boarding school in London. Her friends were also spoilt and would do anything for her.

One day, a girl named Fannie joined their school. She wore dirty clothes, was shabbily dressed and had an old hat on. Everyone could see that Fannie was poor.

Belle and her friends made fun of poor Fannie whenever they got a chance. Fannie was very upset and hurt by the girls' behaviour. However, she was scared to talk to the bullying girls.

One such day, there was poetry recitation and everyone participated. Fannie recited a beautiful poem about friends and friendship. The students were amazed because her poem was the best in the class.

Belle realised her mistake now. Fannie was poor but very nice and talented. Belle apologised to her for her mean behaviour. Fannie forgave her and they became good friends.

6. Suzanne's Friends

Once, there lived a little girl named Suzanne. She had many friends.

One day, Suzanne fell very sick. She could not go out to play with her friends now. She did not have the energy to even get up and walk.

Her friends came to know about her illness. They visited her house every day. They brought beautiful flowers and books for her. Some of them even sat at her bedside and read out stories to her.

When Suzanne started feeling better, she could get up and sit on her bed. Her friends took her out for walks in the meadows. It was spring and Suzanne felt happy to see the butterflies and colourful flowers. They also brought tasty puddings and pies for her to eat. Soon, Suzanne's health improved. She thanked her friends, for it was because of their help that she got better. It is good to have friends!

7. Susie's Prayer

One day, at school, all the children decided to play a game of Squirrel Hunt. Everyone gathered in a circle except for Susie, who was standing in the corner.

Ned Graham became the leader of the group, as he was the biggest and tallest. He said, "We will not let Susie play! Her Father has bad habits. He is always drunk!"

Susie was very upset at these words. She ran home, crying, to her mother.

In the evening, her father returned home from work. He noticed that Susie was sad and asked her what had happened. She told him about Ned's rudeness. This made Susie's Father very sad.

After dinner, Father heard a soft voice from the garden. He saw Susie praying to God to help her Father get rid of his bad habit.

Father was so touched by Susie's prayer that he vowed never to drink again.

8. The Stolen Orange

There was once a girl called Flora.

One day, some guests were coming to Flora's house. Flora was busy cleaning her room. Just then, she passed the kitchen and saw oranges piled up in a dish.

Flora was not allowed to eat those oranges, as her Mother had bought them for the guests. But, she took one and hid it in her pocket.

However, she knew she had done the wrong thing by stealing. Flora wanted to return the orange but the guests arrived and she became busy. She had to play with their children.

Flora could not enjoy any of the games. She kept thinking of how shameful it would be, if the orange fell out of her pocket while they were playing! Or if she sat on it by mistake!

After dinner, Flora went to her Mother. She told her what she had done and asked for her forgiveness. Her Mother was very happy at her honesty. She hugged Flora and forgave her.

9. The Joy of Christmas

Nellie and Adele were decorating the Christmas tree in their living room. Nellie said, "Have you made your Christmas wish?"

"I have written to Santa, but I won't tell you!" Adele said.

The girls were very excited that Christmas was almost there. When they hung up all the decorations on the tree, Nellie said, "Let's make cards for our friends!"

So, the girls started making cards for each of their friends, wishing them a Happy Christmas and New Year. They used bright paints and craft paper.

Then, Adele said, "Nellie, now I am making one for you. But you have to wait until Christmas to open it."

"I'll make one for you, too. You will be surprised when you see it!" said Nellie.

Laughing, the two girls finished their cards and went to bed. Both were very happy and understood that the true spirit of Christmas was sharing and caring.

10. Christmas Presents

It was Christmas Eve. The Smith family had put up their glorious six feet Christmas tree in the living room. It was decorated with fir and pine cones, coloured eggshells, and different shapes cut out of craft paper. The shapes looked like snowflakes. There was a beautiful star on top.

In the evening, the Smith family enjoyed a delicious six-course dinner. Grace and Bella helped their mother clean up after dinner. Then, they hung up their stockings and left cookies and milk by the fireplace for Santa Claus. They went to bed, hoping Santa would leave presents for them.

Grace and Bella's parents knew that they had been good children all year. After the girls were asleep, they put big presents under the Christmas tree for them. In the morning, Grace and Bella were very happy. They decided to be good children next year, too.

11. A Gift for Mother

Emma, Jo and Suzie were sisters. Emma was the oldest. She was a very wise and mature child. She always knew what was best for her and for others. She took good care of her sisters.

It was their Mother's birthday in a few days. They decided to give her a present. "What should we give Mother?" asked Jo.

"I wonder what she wants…" said Suzie.

Emma was quiet. She did not say anything. She was in deep thought. Jo asked, "Emma, what do you think? What should we give Mother?"

Emma said, "I think Mother once mentioned she needed a new apron."

Thus, the girls broke their piggy bank and bought a beautiful blue and yellow flowered apron for their Mother. Emma wrapped it in golden paper and tied a red ribbon around it.

When they presented the gift to their Mother, she had tears of happiness in her eyes.

12. The Wise Teacher

Mrs. Joel taught a class of six-year olds. She loved her class and was very patient with the children. She frequently reminded them that they were all friends and that friends never harm each other.

However, not all children followed what she said. Alicia was one of the children who never listened.

Meg sat next to Alicia. Alicia had taken Meg's book. When Meg asked for it, Alicia lied, "I don't know where the book is. I did not take it."

Meg went to Mrs. Joel and told her about Alicia.

Mrs. Joel asked, "Alicia, did you take Meg's book?"

"No, I did not!" lied Alicia again.

"Fine, Alicia. Find Meg's book, or you will have to give her your book!" said wise Mrs. Joel.

Alicia returned Meg's book. Then on, Alicia learnt that to harm others would harm us also. Hence, she stopped troubling Meg and other children.

13. Katie's Yard

It was spring. Beautiful flowers were blooming in pink and white. The wind was cool and the Sun was shedding its warm rays on the Earth.

Katie was a little girl who lived with her parents in a small but beautiful house. She was very happy that she would finally get to play in the yard after the long, cold winter.

Katie admired the beautiful tulips in her yard. She told her Mother, "Mother, look at those pink, yellow and red buds!"

"You are right, dear," said her Mother. "They are indeed beautiful!"

Then, Katie asked, "Mother, can I feed the birds?" Her Mother went into the house and brought out a small bird-house and hung it up on the tree. Then Katie filled it with bird feed. The birds crowded around the bird-house.

Katie felt very happy to see the birds chirping in her bird-house and singing around her tulips.

14. The Little Red Ball

Josie was playing in the park when she found a red ball. 'A little red ball! I will keep it for myself,' thought Josie. She kicked the ball all over the park and had fun. As she was playing, she heard someone crying.

She turned around and saw a small girl crying. She said, "Hello. I am Josie. Why are you crying?"

The small girl said, through, big, weepy eyes, "I am Mia. I have lost my favourite red ball."

Josie was confused. 'Should I return the ball or keep it for myself ?' she thought. 'But it belongs to her and she is so sad!'

So, Josie showed the ball to Mia and asked, "Is this your ball?"

"Oh! Yes! Thank you!" said Mia and took the ball. Her face was happily shining now.

Mia and Josie became friends. Every day, they played with the little red ball, together.

15. Big Sister Lucy

Lucy and Meg were sisters. One day, they returned from the park. Their Mother said, "Girls, please wash your hands and come to the table."

Meg, the younger of the girls said, "I don't want to wash up, Mother!"

Their Mother said, "It is best for you to clean your hands after playing outside. Look at those hands. They are dirty. You cannot have your pancakes with dirty hands."

"I do not need to wash my hands; I will be eating with fork and knife!" said Meg.

Lucy was watching this quietly. She told her sister, "Meg, your hands have brought dirt from outside. Just look at them! Do you know, so many germs live in dirt? They are on your hands now!"

Meg was scared. She looked at her hands and said, "Gosh! I didn't know that!"

"Come with me. I shall help you wash your hands," said Lucy.

The girls washed up and Meg felt better and cleaner. Their Mother was very proud of her wise little daughters.

16. The Careless Sisters

Joan and Ella were playing with their dolls in the living room. Mother said, "Grandpa is coming. Please put your toys away."

Joan said, "Sure, Mummy," and started putting away the dolls.

Ella suddenly said, "Joan! We have to go to the backyard for our tea party. Come!" Thus, the girls forgot to put away their dolls and rushed to the backyard.

In a while, the doorbell rang. Mother opened the door for Grandpa. Joan and Ella ran and hugged him.

Joan said, "Grandpa, please play with us!"

As they walked into the living room, Grandpa slipped on a doll and fell down.

Everyone was worried. Mother helped Grandpa get up. Then she scolded the children, "I asked you to put away your dolls. See, Grandpa is hurt because of you!"

The girls felt very bad. They said, "We are very sorry. We will listen to you from now."

17. Jessie's Drawing

Jessie was excited. She loved to colour and now she had a new pack of crayons. She started drawing on the wall.

Jessie drew the sun, some trees and birds. She also drew some beautiful flowers. She was very happy to see her colourful drawings.

As soon as she had finished, she called her Mother and said, "Mother, look what I have drawn. Isn't it beautiful?"

Jessie's Mother was shocked to see that her daughter had drawn on the walls. She said, "It is a wonderful drawing, Jessie. But, I am sorry we cannot save it. I told you to draw in your drawing book. I have to clean the wall now. Next time, remember to draw on a piece of paper."

Thus, Mother wiped the wall and the drawings, too. Jessie felt very sad because her beautiful drawings were gone now. She decided never to draw on walls again.

18. Clever Danika

Danika was fond of her younger sister, Emma. Emma was a very kind girl, but she was careless. She never made her bed, cleaned her room or did her homework on time. Danika was just the opposite. She always put things away and was hard working.

Their Father was a rich man. Thus, they had a Servant to clean the house. The Servant took care of the mess that Emma made. Danika tried telling her little sister to take care of her things, but she never listened.

One day, Danika decided to teach Emma a lesson. She told the Servant to take a day off.

That day, there was no one to clean up after Emma. By night, her room was a mess. The next day, Emma could not find her books, school uniform and colours. She realised her mistake and promised to be responsible and do her chores, herself.

19. Caring Bess

Dora loved her big sister, Bess. She followed Bess wherever she went. Dora liked to be with Bess even when she played with her friends. Soon, Bess was bored of having Dora around all the time. She wanted to play alone with her friends, sometimes.

So, Bess said, "Dora, it is time that you make your own friends. You'll have fun with little girls of your age." But Dora did not know how to make friends. She was scared to go out and talk to other children.

Thus, Bess took Dora to the park, one evening. There, she saw her friend, Laura and her little sister, Kelly. She introduced Dora and Kelly. The four girls played together for a while.

The little girls happily played together. Soon, Dora and Kelly became best friends. Soon, they also made other friends at the park. Bess was very happy for her sister.

20. Truthful Lisa

Melanie and Lisa were taking their evening nap. Their Mother was washing clothes.

When she finished her work, she went to the girls' room and said, "Wake up, girls. It is time for your snack."

Sometime later, Mother went in the kitchen to see if Melanie and Lisa had finished their milk and cookies. However, she was shocked to find the cookie jar broken. She called the girls and asked, "Which one of you broke the cookie jar?"

"I didn't even enter the kitchen, Mother," said Melanie.

"I did not do it!" said Lisa.

Mother said, "Unless you tell the truth, you will not get snacks or toys."

Then, Lisa slowly said, "Mother, I'm sorry. I tried to get a cookie and accidentally dropped the jar."

Mother said, "I am glad you told the truth. Help me clean the broken pieces and I'll give you both cookies."

21. Wise Gracie

Gracie and Norma were sisters. Gracie was the younger one, but she knew how to take care of herself and things around the house. She was very sensible and wise. Though Norma was older, she could not make decisions. She always needed help from her Mother.

One day, when Mother was out, their neighbour and friend, Mrs. Smith came over. Norma answered the door. Mrs. Smith asked her if the girls wanted to go on a picnic with the Smith family. Norma did not know what to say.

Gracie came forward and told Mrs. Smith, "Thank you very much for inviting us. But, since our Mother is out, we cannot leave the house without her."

When Mother returned, she was very happy to know about Gracie's decision. Norma also realised that she should be smart and take the right decisions. She decided to observe Gracie and learn from her.

22. Joan's Delay

One day, a group of little girls was playing at the park. They were having so much fun that they did not realise how much time went by. The sun was setting already. Suddenly, one of the girls, Elizabeth, noticed that it was getting dark. She told her friends that it was probably time to go home.

All of them, except Joan, agreed and they went home. Joan enjoyed playing on the swing so much that she did not want to leave.

Soon, it was night and almost supper-time. Joan's Mother called at their friends' and neighbours' houses and asked them if Joan was there. She was very worried and went to the park. She found Joan playing on the swing and told her, "Joan, you are still here! I have been worried sick! I called your friends to find out what happened. You should always return home before dark!"

Joan saw how worried her Mother was. She felt guilty and promised to be home on time.

23. Maria's Perfect Evening

One day, Mrs. Bogus invited Mrs. Lee and her family over for dinner. Maria Bogus was excited that her best friend was coming. She offered to help her Mother with the preparations.

Maria went to the market and bought bread, beautiful flowers and a basket of fresh fruits. When she came home, she arranged the flowers in her favourite vase. She placed the vase on the centre table. It looked beautiful.

Maria saw her Mother getting ready to bake a cake. "Are you making cake for dessert?" she asked.

Mrs. Bogus said, "Yes, my dear. You can help, too!" Thus, Maria and her Mother baked a delicious cake.

Then, Maria went up to her room and found her favourite frock with lace and buttons. Maria put it on and looked pretty as a fairy. In the evening, the Lee family came and they all had a wonderful time!

24. Florentina's Riddle

Florentina's friends were having a sleep-over at her house. After a tasty dinner and delicious desserts, they sat in the moonlit garden.

The girls wanted to do something interesting. Florentina asked her friends to answer a riddle. "Girls, there is a 'Gate' that will open and close as one desires. The smart ones use this Gate, very wisely. All things that enter this Gate get a red carpet welcome. There is a well at the end of this slippery carpet. Once something goes down this well, it never returns. Who knows what the 'Gate' is?"

Florentina's friends thought hard but could not come up with the answer. They said, "Florentina, Can you take us to see this Gate?"

Florentina said, "Why not? I will show it to you right away!" and she opened her mouth.

Now they understood that 'Gate' meant the 'mouth' and carpet meant the 'tongue'!

25. The Three Friends

Kate, Pansy and Hima were good friends. They went to the same school. Every day, they walked to school together. On their way back from school, they would stop to pick beautiful flowers and sweet blackberries.

One morning, as they started walking towards their school, it started raining. Kate and Pansy had remembered their umbrellas. Hima did not have hers.

Kate said, "Hima, come under my umbrella. Don't get wet in the rain."

"Yes Hima! You might catch a cold. We'll share. Come under one of our umbrellas," said Pansy.

Hima was very happy to have such good friends. On the way back from school, she stopped and picked daisies and other flowers. She made two beautiful little bouquets and gave them to Kate and Pansy. "I am glad to have such good friends!" smiled Hima.

Looking at the three friends, other children also started sharing their umbrellas with others!

26. Bertha's Grandmother

Bertha Gilbert lived with her family in a little village called Hillside.

One day, her wealthy friend, Holly visited Bertha's house with her Mother.

While having tea, Bertha noticed the old, worn-out furniture they had. She glanced at her Grandmother. She wore simple clothes and was knitting quietly. Holly and her Mother, on the other hand, wore bright dresses of silk and wore precious jewels.

Bertha also noticed Holly look at the house and make faces. She was not pleased.

After the guests had left Bertha went to her Mother and said, "Grandma should wear fancy clothes! Holly was making faces at her!"

Mother was very upset with Bertha. She said, "Bertha, you should respect people the way they are and not for what they wear."

Bertha felt ashamed of herself, for her Grandmother was wise, caring and loving. She also decided to not have ill-mannered friends like Holly, any more.

27. Cousin Janet's Problem

There was once a naughty girl called Pommy. The children in her class were afraid of her. Her teachers had given up hope of making her a well-mannered girl. People tried to teach her good manners, but she would not change.

Pommy's cousin, Janet was very troubled by her behaviour and prayed for her.

One day, Janet's Mother asked her to carry some buttermilk for her Aunt Nancy.

On her way, Janet saw a cow blocking the path. She was very afraid of cows and began to shout for help.

Suddenly, Pommy came and chased away the cow with a stick. Pommy then went with Janet to Aunt Nancy's house, in case there were more cows on the way. She also walked back home with her.

Janet's Mother thanked Pommy, and she felt very good. From that day on, Pommy changed and became a nice girl.

28. The Lion in Love

Once, a Woodcutter lived in a village. He went to the nearby forest to cut wood every day.

One day, he took his daughter to help him. While they both were cutting wood, a Lion saw the Woodcutter's daughter and fell in love with her.

The next day, the Lion went to the Woodcutter's house and said, "Dear Woodcutter, I am in love with your daughter. Do let me marry her!"

The Woodcutter knew that the Lion had sharp teeth and would hurt his daughter. So, he said, "Indeed, you can marry my daughter. First, go and cut your sharp teeth and nails, for she is scared of them."

The Lion went to the forest and got his nails and teeth cut. When, he returned to the village again, the Woodcutter was no longer afraid of him. He beat the Lion with his stick and drove him back to the forest.

29. The Paper Kite

A beautiful Paper Kite was flying high in the sky. It was brightly coloured, with curly tassels and a long string. The Kite was so high up that it was giddy with excitement.

The Kite thought, 'O look at me flying so gracefully! If I were free, I could go far away.'

The Kite tugged at its string, as it wanted to fly right through the clouds and above the eagles. However, the string was strong and held it tight.

The Kite impatiently tugged at its string again and again and the string broke.

The Kite was full of joy. It tried to fly higher, but suddenly it started falling. Free of its string, it had become heavy and lost control. It drifted towards the sea and was washed away in the tide.

The Paper Kite cried, "I wanted to fly higher and higher. Look, what I got for being so proud!"

30. The Proud Lady and the Caterpillar

One day, a young Lady was walking in her beautiful garden and admiring the colourful flowers. Suddenly, the Lady saw a Caterpillar on her dress. She was horrified.

The Lady shook him off her dress, saying angrily, "Go away, you ugly Caterpillar! You eat all the leaves, flowers and fruits and ruin my lovely garden. I work so hard to keep my garden beautiful. You spoil it by being here."

The Caterpillar looked at her and said calmly, "Proud Lady, the lovely silk of your dress has come from insects like me, so do not insult me. I am ugly to look at now. Soon, I shall turn into a beautiful Butterfly. Your beauty is temporary and depends only on the clothes you wear. I am beautiful from inside and when I become a Butterfly I will be more beautiful than you!"

1. Jealous Mrs. Plum

Mrs. Plum was jealous of beautiful Mrs. Peach. One day, she invited Mrs. Peach over for dinner. She made soup for dinner but put a lot of chillies in it.

When Mrs. Peach arrived, Mrs. Plum greeted her politely and was very nice to her. However, she really wanted Mrs. Peach to eat the soup full of chillies and burn her throat. Soon, she served the soup. Like a true lady, Mrs. Peach did not complain.

Later, Mrs. Peach invited Mrs. Plum to have dessert at her place. Mrs. Peach baked a pie, but put a lot of salt in it. Thus, when she served it to Mrs. Plum, she found it very salty and could not eat any of it. Now Mrs. Plum began to cry. To this, Mrs. Peach said, "If you play dirty tricks on people, then you must expect them to do the same to you."

2. Little Red-Cap

Once, a little girl named Red-Cap lived in the village. She loved her Grandmother dearly, and would visit her every Sunday.

One day, Red-Cap's Mother said, "Red-Cap, your Grandma is ill. Take this cake and wine to her cottage in the woods. Do not travel away from the road, and do not talk to any strangers."

Thus, Red-Cap set out for her Grandmother's cottage. Soon, a Wolf saw her from behind a bush. He said, "Good morning, little girl! Where are you going?" Red-Cap told him about her ill Grandmother.

The wicked Wolf said, "Little girl, the forest has many beautiful flowers. You should take them for your Grandmother!"

Red-Cap now saw that there really were plenty of pretty flowers. She left the road and went inside the forest to collect some flowers for her Grandmother.

Meanwhile, the Wolf went to Grandmother's cottage and gobbled her up! Then, he dressed as Grandmother and waited.

When Red-Cap arrived at the cottage, she said, "Ooh! Grandma, you have such big ears!"

The Wolf said, "So, that I can hear you well, dear."

Red-Cap then said, "You have such big eyes, too!"

The Wolf said, "So, that I can see you well."

Red-Cap asked, "Why do you have such big teeth, Grandma?"

The Wolf said, "So, that I can eat you!" and he jumped at Red-Cap and gobbled her up as well!

A Hunter was passing by the cottage. When he saw the door open, he went inside and found the Wolf. He shot him dead. Then, he quickly picked up a big knife and cut the Wolf 's stomach. From it, Red-Cap and her Grandmother came out.

Red-Cap said, "My Mother asked me to stay on the road and not to talk to strangers. I did not listen to her. From now on, I shall always obey my Mother."

3. Silly Catherine

Catherine was a careless and silly young rabbit. Whenever she went out, she often forgot to close the door behind her. One day, she had to go out of the house to buy lunch for her husband, Joseph.

As Catherine was leaving, Joseph said, "Don't forget the door, dear." Catherine thought about her husband's words and an idea came to her. 'The best way not to forget the door is to take it with me!'

Thus, Catherine took off the door from its hinges and heaved it onto her back. She went to the market carrying the door. Everybody started laughing at her. This made her feel very bad.

Now Catherine realised that Joseph meant her to close the door and not take it with her. 'I will be more careful now and pay attention to what others tell me,' she decided.

4. The Moon's Glow

Once, there lived a handsome Prince high in the ountains. He loved nature and often strolled in the mountains to look at the flowers, the clouds and the sunset.

However, the Prince's favourite was the moon. He loved the moon's gentle glow. His great wish was to visit the moon and see where the glow came from.

Once, the Prince met a kind Witch who gave him the magic spell to visit the moon. His dream had finally come true! When he reached the moon, he saw that its light came from the beautiful Moon Princess.

The two fell in love and danced in the silver glow. Together, they created a little silver flower. It grew and many more silver flowers blossomed from it. Then, the Moon Princess spread them over the moon so that it would glow more. Then, she and the Prince got married and lived happily on earth. The silver flowers continued to glow on the moon.

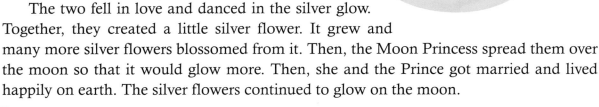

5. Delicious Cakes

Once, there lived a powerful and cruel King.

One day, he saw a beautiful girl and wanted to marry her. The Girl did not want to marry him and asked her Stepmother to help her escape. But the Stepmother was very greedy and wanted the Girl to marry the King, so that she could become rich. So, the Girl decided to run away. She slipped out of her house at night and travelled to another country.

The Girl reached an inn. The innkeeper kept her as a cook. The Girl started baking cakes at the inn. Her cakes were so tasty that she became very popular.

One day, the Prince of that country visited the inn. When he tasted the cakes, he found them to be very delicious. "I want to meet the person who has baked these cakes!" he said.

Thus, the Girl was presented before the Prince. He fell in love with her at first sight. They were soon married and lived happily.

6. Naughty Janine

Joan and Lisa were best friends. One day, they went for a picnic to a river. They took a basket of food and some toys. Joan's little sister, Janine, also wanted to go with them. Joan said, "You can come, but promise to stay near us." Janine readily promised.

Soon, the three girls reached the river. They started playing with their dolls. At mid-day, the two friends started to lay down their lunch.

Janine saw that they were busy, so she quietly went in the nearby forest. As she walked deep into the forest, Janine lost her way. She tried to run back to the river but she could not find the right way.

Janine started crying and shouting out for help. Joan and Lisa had been looking for her. Soon, they found her. Janine said, "I have learnt that I should listen to you, for you are older and know better."

7. The Wise Queen

One day, Queen Jade was walking in her garden. Suddenly, she noticed two Squirrels quarrelling among themselves. The larger Squirrel was white. The other was smaller and black with long, sharp teeth. Just as the Black Squirrel was about to bite the White Squirrel and kill it, Queen Jade threw a stone at it and killed it. Safe at last, the White Squirrel went off into the trees.

Sometime later, a Blue Fairy appeared out of the forest. She told Queen Jade that she was the White Squirrel. The Black Squirrel was an evil witch.

"I would like to offer you a gift for helping me. Do you want gold and jewels?"

"I do not want jewels, but wisdom," replied the sweet Queen.

"You shall have it always," smiled the Blue Fairy.

Thus, Queen Jade became the wisest queen in the world and was loved by all her subjects.

8. Mopsey's Mistake

One cold evening, Uncle came to visit Louie and her family. He asked Louie, "So, Mopsey, where is Popsey?" Uncle had the habit of calling everyone by funny names. Popsey was Louie's little sister, Grace.

Louie replied, "Popsey is sleeping."

Uncle then handed her two candy sticks and said, "Well, if she were awake, she would have got some candy, too."

Mother saw Louie eat the candy and asked her, "Aren't you going to save some for your sister?"

"Candy is not for small girls. Besides, I want it all for myself," replied Louie.

Just then, Grace woke up and came into the room. Uncle handed her two candy sticks from his pocket. Grace offered the bigger stick to Louie.

Louie was ashamed of the way she had behaved and said to Grace, "I will never be greedy again and will share everything I have with you, always."

9. True Friendship

One summer afternoon, the bell rang in the school. It was time for the last lesson of the day—spellings.

Eunice was a bright, blue-eyed girl. The Master asked her to spell 'laughter'. She spelt it correctly. Unfortunately, the Master did not hear her and passed the answer. Eunice softly said to her friend, Emma, "But I spelt it right!"

However, the Master heard Eunice whispering. He called her name and said, "Eunice, come and stand in front of the class. When you spot another person whispering, you can sit and he can stand in your place."

Eunice could not find a whispering student to take her place. She looked sad so Emma looked at her and pointed to herself. The Master saw Emma whisper, so he made Emma stand and Eunice sit.

Eunice was very grateful to her true friend Emma. The two remained friends all their lives.

10. Patty's Secret

Patty had been very sick and had to go to the Doctor many times in the past. She would be scared earlier. However, now she was very brave and always smiled in the hospital

One day, Patty overheard her Aunt tell her parents about a sick Girl who was afraid of visiting the Doctor.

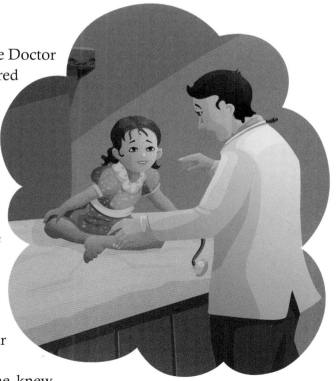

Patty went to visit this little Girl with her parents. Patty said to the Girl, "I have to go to the Doctor many times and I used to be very scared. But, one night, I had a dream where I saw God. He told me not to worry. Then when I visited the Doctor the next time, I felt God put his hand on my head and say 'Patty, I am taking away your fear and pain.' "

The Girl was no longer scared, for she knew God was taking away her fear and pain, too, just like he did Patty's.

11. Friends

One day, few friends met after the school in the evening. The First Friend looked very sad and upset.

The others asked, "What happened? Why are you so upset?"

The First Friend said, "I am sad. My best Friend has stopped talking to me. She has made a new friend and spends most of her time with her."

The other Friends looked at each other. They said, "But you always misbehaved and fought with her!"

The First Friend did not understand. So, one of them explained, "Friends are very precious. One should always respect them. They should never be taken for granted."

Now, the First Friend realised her mistake.

The other Friends smiled kindly at her and said, "You should apologise to her for your misbehaviour. Then promise to be polite. We are sure that she will forgive you."

The First Friend apologised and won her best Friend back.

12. A Little Girl's Difficulty

A Little Girl lived with her Mother in a small house. Her Mother worked hard to send her to the best school in town. She wanted her daughter to have the best of education.

One day, the Girl came back from school with tears in her eyes. The Mother asked her why she was crying. She said, "My friend has invited all the classmates to her birthday party tonight. But I have been ignored because I am not rich like them and do not have expensive clothes."

The Mother kissed her and said, "One should not bother about people who make friends on the basis of money. If your friend did not invite you because you are poor then she does not deserve to be your friend."

The Little Girl understood and wiped her tears. She said, "You are right, Mother. I do not need such false friends."

13. The Greedy Woman

Once, there lived a poor Woman. One day, the Woman went to the market and bought a beautiful hen. To her surprise, the hen laid a silver egg, the next day!

The Woman was amazed. She went to the town Jeweller who confirmed that the egg was indeed made of real silver. The Woman sold the egg to him and made a good sum of money. She went to the market and bought new clothes and a delicious cake.

Now, the Woman thought, 'If the hen could somehow be made to lay more than one egg each day, I would never have to work again!'

Therefore, the Woman decided that the hen must eat more, so that it could lay more eggs. So she forced the hen to eat a lot. The result was that the hen did not lay any eggs, but died of indigestion! The Woman was now left with regret for her greed.

14. The Perfect Match

Once, there lived a Shepherd in the village. He had a beautiful Daughter. He wanted her to be married to a good and kind Man.

One day, three Men came to meet the Shepherd. They all wanted to marry his Daughter. They were handsome and had magical powers. The first Man said that he could fly in the sky and go anywhere. The second Man could go under water and travel through sea and the third Man could talk to the animals on land.

Just then, a servant came and said that a snake had bitten the Shepherd's Daughter and she had died.

The Shepherd started crying in sorrow. However, the third Man called out to the snake, at once. The snake went to the Daughter and swallowed back its poison. The Daughter was alive, again.

The Shepherd married his Daughter to the third Man, who had saved her life.

15. The Fairy and the Witch

Once, there was an evil Witch in the countryside who stole children. She found two little Girls playing by the river and put them in her prison.

One day, the Girls succeeded in escaping. Now, the evil Witch set off to bring them back. A good Fairy, who was passing by, saw the little Girls running and took pity on them. She set a great ring of fire around them to keep them safe, but the Witch used black magic to blow out the flames.

Now, the Fairy was angry, for the Witch was trying to hurt such sweet Girls. She built a high wall of glass around the Girls. It was so smooth, it could not be climbed.

The Witch returned to her house to find a hammer to break the wall. But, by the time she returned, the Fairy had carried the Girls away safely to their home.

16. The Brave Woman

Once, there was a Thief, who had stolen a bell and was running away with it. As he was running through the forest, he was eaten by a tiger. The bell was found by the monkeys, who began to ring it. The noise frightened the people of the nearby village, who thought it was the sound of a demon.

A wise Woman lived in that village. She knew that there was no demon in the forest and that it was certainly an animal. She decided to rid the villagers of their fear.

Thus, she went out with a basket of fruit. When she heard the bell, she left the fruit basket on the ground and hid. Soon, the monkeys threw themselves on the fruit basket. Quickly, the woman picked up the bell and ran back to the village.

When the Woman reached the village, she was praised for her courage!

17. The Miserly Woman and the Wise Woman

Once, there lived a Miserly Woman. She would always try to have everything, without spending her money.

One day, she went to a Wise Woman. She said, "Dear friend, please let me borrow your pot, for mine is broken."

The Wise Woman said, "I will lend you my pot, but only if you lend me your best gown." The Miserly Woman agreed.

At home, the Miserly Woman thought, 'This pot is so large and strong. I want to keep it.'

The next day, she gave a much smaller pot to the Wise Woman and said, "It is the son of your pot and was born during the night."

The Wise Woman said, "I cannot return your best gown, for it died last night."

The Miserly Woman angrily said, "A gown cannot die!"

"If a pot can have a son, then a gown can surely die!" replied the Wise Woman.

18. Clever Oedipus

A long time ago, the city of Thebes was guarded by a Sphinx. A Sphinx is a creature with the head of a woman, the body of a lion and the wings of an eagle.

Whenever a traveller reached the gates of Thebes, the Sphinx asked him a riddle. If he gave the wrong answer, she would eat them.

One day, clever Oedipus reached the gates of Thebes. The Sphinx asked him, "What being has four legs in the morning, two at mid-day and three in the evening?"

O "Man!" Oedipus answered, "The morning of his life is when he is a child. He crawls on four legs then. Youth is the mid-day of his life, when he walks on two legs. Finally, the evening of his life comes when he is old. Then, he uses a stick which becomes his third leg."

The Sphinx smiled and let Oedipus enter Thebes.

19. The Moon's Jealousy

Thousands of years ago, the Moon felt jealous of the Sun, for the Sun was very bright, while the Moon only had a faint glow. Thus, Moon decided to shine as bright as the Sun. It sparkled with all its might and matched the Sun's light.

Now, this meant that there was always light, throughout the night. Thus, mankind could not tell when it was day and when evening or night.

This caused all kinds of problems. People never knew when it was time to get up or when it was time to go to bed. They did not know when to have lunch or when to have dinner.

The Lord realised what was happening. At once, he ordered Archangel Gabriel to spread his wings and veil the light of the Moon. Gabriel obeyed and shielded the Moon's light. Soon, Moon controlled his jealousy and went back to glowing faintly.

20. The Grateful Eagle

Once, there lived a kind girl named Beth.

One day, she went to the forest to collect firewood. On the way, she saw an Eagle caught in a trap. She, at once, set it free and walked on.

Beth became tired and sat down on a rock on top of a hill. The Eagle was flying close by and she saw that the rock was loose and would roll down the hill, taking Beth with it.

Thus, while Beth was having her lunch, the Eagle swooped down and snatched her hat. It then flew away with it. Beth stood up and ran down the hill after the bird.

Just as Beth reached a safe distance away from the rock on which she had been sitting, it rolled down the hill with a loud crash. She realised then that the grateful Eagle had paid back for her kindness. Then on, Beth and the Eagle became good friends.

21. The Rose and the Amaranth

Once, there was a beautiful garden. It was spring and all the flowers in the garden were in full bloom. Among the many rows of flowers and shrubs, rows of Amaranths and Roses grew side by side.

An Amaranth, which was growing beside a Rose, said, one day, "How beautiful you look, dear Rose! Such bright colour and so pretty to look at! You are the delight of the Gods, of young maids and of lovers. You are the favourite of bouquets. I envy your shapeliness and your perfume!"

To this, the Rose replied, "Oh, Amaranth! I live only for a few days and even if no one picks me, I still wither and die. You, on the other hand, are useful to man and are always in blossom. You live forever!"

The Amaranth understood that it was better to be useful and live forever, rather than be beautiful and live briefly.

22. The Evil Gnomes

Once, there lived a Woman in the country. She had a beautiful baby Girl, but the Evil Gnomes stole the child. They put a baby Gnome in the cradle in her place.

The Woman found the Evil Gnomes while looking for her baby Girl. She begged them to return her baby to her, but they just laughed cruelly. Sad and distracted without her baby, the Woman put a raw egg in the fire instead of the pot of water. This created a sudden burst of fire.

The Evil Gnomes were afraid of light. Upon seeing the fire burst, they jumped with fear. They thought that the Woman was aware of their fears and would finish them. Thus, they returned the baby back to her. Then, they apologised to the Woman and took away the baby Gnome.

The happy Woman took her baby Girl in her arms and hugged her tight.

23. The Impatient Girls

Once, a woman lived with her three daughters. The Girls were very impatient and never listened to their Mother.

One day, it was the birthday of the youngest Girl. The Mother prepared her favourite strawberry cake. When the cake was baked, the Mother took it out of the oven. She topped it with chocolate icing. Then, she decorated the cake with little red roses.

The Girls' mouths watered when they saw it. "Dear Mother, kind Mother, hurry up and give us a slice!" the impatient Girls begged her.

"Wait until it cools down and you can eat it all, otherwise, your tongue will burn," said the Mother.

However, the impatient Girls could not wait and tried to eat it hot. The moment they put a pieces of the cake in their mouths, their tongue were burnt!

They went to their Mother and cried in pain, "Oh! We will always obey you!"

24. The Poppy Princess

Once, there lived a beautiful Princess. All her subjects loved her, for she was wise and just.

One day, a jealous and evil Witch turned her into a poppy flower. Each evening, she returned to her human form and roamed the fields.

One night, a handsome Prince was riding across the field. He saw the Princess and fell in love with her. She said to him, "You can break the spell by picking me up when I am a poppy. But, you must find me and pick me at the first go."

The next morning, the Prince saw that there were thousands of poppies in the field. He thought, 'The Princess becomes human at night. Thus, she will be the only poppy that would not be wet with dew.'

Soon, he found the dry poppy and picked it. The spell was broken and the Prince and the Princess were married.

25. Carrie's Master

One Sunday, Miss Evans told the children, "In some countries, there was a custom where the servants were marked with the names of their masters on their arms. In this way the masters and their servants could easily identify each other. But now we do not have any masters. We are the servants of God. And God tells if we are his true servants."

While walking home, Carrie overheard Belle and Jenny gossiping. Carrie reminded them of the lesson they had learnt that day. She then asked God, "Please show me if I am your true servant."

That evening, her brother Charlie, took her book to read, as he found his rather boring. This made Carrie very angry and she snatched it out of his hand.

As soon as she opened the book, she saw the sentence, "You have need of patience."

Carrie immediately realised her mistake and gave the book back to Charlie. Now she understood one had to practise patience to be a true servant of God.

26. A Girl's Song

Once, there was a terrible accident in Scranton, Pennsylvania. A few Miners had been buried underground and attempts to rescue them had proven unfruitful.

The Mining Community did not know what more they could do to rescue their fellow Miners. They only had sympathy left to offer to the families of the buried Miners.

On the evening of the third day, many people gathered at the mouth of the mine. There was no proof that these men were still alive. So people just stood there in sorrow.

There was a little girl who stood in a corner. She began to sing softly. Her voice was so sweet and sad that the people began searching once again. By morning, all buried men were found alive and safe.

The little Girl, however, was never seen in the town again. To this day, the people of Scranton believe that she was an Angel.

27. Elizabeth's Wish

Elizabeth was unhappy. She lived in a small house in the city of Oaktown. Elizabeth wished her father had more money to get her everything she wished for.

Every day, Elizabeth's parents sat on their porch at sunset. She would play in the garden.

One evening, the sunset was just gorgeous. Mother said, "Elizabeth, see how beautiful the sunset is!"

But Elizabeth was lost in her thoughts. She said, "Father, I see the beautiful house with the golden windows over there. Why can't we have a house like that?"

"Come, I'll take you up the hill to see the house," said Dad.

As they climbed up the hill, the golden windows disappeared. Elizabeth realised that the sun's rays had made the windows look golden. Now she understood that money and riches are only good from a distance. Close up, they are ordinary things and one should not be unhappy for money.

28. Wise Meg

Meg was a very helpful, sweet girl. She loved to play with her friends. One day, she went over to her friend Jane's house to play. Soon, the ice-cream man visited the streets.

Jane asked her mother to buy her icecream. But her mother did not have money. So she said, "When your father is back, we shall go to the store and buy ice-cream."

Jane was very upset at this and started crying. She would not listen to her mother. Her mother did not know what to do. Meg felt very sorry for Jane and her mother.

She said, "Come Jane, let's go my house. I think my father is at home."

The girls went to Meg's house and asked her father for ice-cream. He bought them ice-cream and made Jane promise that she would never trouble her mother again. Now the girls were happy.

29. Regina's Complaint

Regina's Father worked in the bakery. Her mother died when she was born. Her Father left home early every day and returned home for supper.

Regina was left alone at home. She took care of herself and the house, too. Some days, if her Father did not reach home on time, she would even cook supper.

One day, Regina felt very bored doing all the work by herself. She never had a chance to meet the other girls and play with them. So, she visited the park.

A girl came up to Regina and asked, "Are you new here?"

Regina shook her head and told her about the housework she had to do. The Girl said, "You should not feel bad. Your Father works hard all day, you should help him. We can play together in your free time."

Regina happily agreed. Soon, the two girls became best friends.

30. Secret

Once, a girl lived with her Mother. The Mother gave her good values and advised her to be honest, always. One day, the Daughter came back from school with tears in her eyes.

The Mother got worried and asked her the reason. The Daughter did not tell anything and went to her room.

Little later, she came out and hugged her mother. The Mother asked, "What happened, my darling?"

She replied, "I failed in my exams. The result came last week but I did not tell you. Now the Principal does not want me to attend the school."

The Mother said, "A daughter should never keep a secret from her mother. If she does, then she definitely gets into trouble."

The Daughter apologised and promised to be honest in future. The next day, her Mother went and convinced the Principal to let her Daughter attend school.

31. Little Angels

One day, a few girls were playing. They saw a Poor Girl watching them. They felt pity for her and wanted to know about her. So, they followed her and saw her enter a little hut. They also went in.

They said, "We noticed you and thought you were a stranger here. We thought to ask you to join our school. We have such good times and our teachers are very knowledgeable."

The Poor Girl replied, "I would like to go, but my Mother does not have the money."

The girls discussed and said, "We will save our pocket money and pay your fees." The Poor Girl had tears of happiness in her eyes.

Her Mother came and said, "You are little angels for my daughter. Thank you!" The girls comforted them and soon left.

The next day, they collected the money and took the Poor Girl to school.

1. The Moon and the Sun

Little Kelly came running inside the house. She had been out in the garden, looking at the bright full Moon.

"How come I don't see the Moon every night? Why is it not always this large and bright?" Kelly asked her older sister Mia.

Mia said, "When the Moon shines, the Sun feels jealous of its glow. It begins to cut the Moon away, little by little, with a knife. That is why the Moon appears smaller every night. Soon, the Sun chases the Moon away.

The Moon then goes home in discomfort. Then, a few days later, it heals and becomes a new Moon. It then returns to the sky to shine. Soon, it becomes large and round and you see it as you did today! A few days later, the Sun arrives to chase it off again."

Mia finished her story and saw that Kelly was already asleep.

2. Eve's Children

Adam and Eve built themselves a lovely little house after they were banished from Eden. Adam farmed the land, and Eve spun and stitched clothes.

They had a child every year. Some children were beautiful and others, not so beautiful. Some were fair and some were dark. Eve sometimes felt bad when she saw her not-so-beautiful children. However, Eve took as much care as she could of them all, and all the children grew up, healthy and strong.

One day, Adam said, "Be quick. An Angel told me that God wants to visit us and meet our children."

Eve decided she would only show her beautiful, fair children and scrubbed and dressed them in their best clothes. She hid the dark, not-so-beautiful children; some behind the coal scuttle, some behind the haystacks and some under the bed. The house was sparkling clean when God knocked at their door.

Adam opened the door and God walked in. The beautiful children bowed and knelt down. God smiled and blessed them. One became a King, another, a Count and another, the Pope, and in this way, they were made powerful and fortunate.

Then Eve thought, 'If God is so gracious, He will also bless my other children.' She called them out and soon, they stood before God – dark, scruffy and shy children.

God smiled again and started blessing them. One was made a miller, another, a farmer, yet another, an ironsmith, and in this way, all the trades were given to Eve's children.

Eve said, "God, why did you not bless my children equally?"

God said, "If I had, then who would have done the work, grown the food and helped the Kings and Princes to rule over kingdoms?"

Then Eve realised that God was kind and wise, and bowed before him.

3. Love of the Stars

There are millions of stars in the sky. The stars that are close to each other become friends and form groups. These groups of stars are called constellations. Every constellation forms a shape, much like a join-the-dot game!

One such constellation is called Taurus. Aldebaran was the brightest star in this constellation. Now there was another constellation near Taurus, called Pleiades. Electra was the most beautiful star of Pleiades.

Hundreds of years ago, Aldebaran saw Electra and fell in love with her. Thus, one day, he visited her and asked her to marry him. However, on his way, Aldebaran was attacked by another star named Alycon. The two started fighting to win Electra's love.

It is said that they are still fighting, even today. Thus, on a clear night, you can see pale blue Electra followed by red Alycon and Aldebaran, who still hope to win her love!

4. Dina's Tall Tales

Dina was a very brash and dishonest girl. She would tell tall tales to her friends about false adventures and trips.

Soon, Dina's friends became tired of her lies and started ignoring her whenever she spoke. Thus, Dina decided to go and stay with her Aunt in Boreville in her summer holidays.

A few months later, Dina returned from Boreville. One day, she invited all her friends for tea. Just as they all sat down to tea, Dina said, "In Boreville, I jumped so high, I was out of sight! If you don't believe me, go and ask anyone who was there."

"There is no need," said a girl. "Why don't you pretend you are in Boreville and jump out of sight right now?"

Everybody started laughing. Dina realised that people hated her lies. She felt ashamed of herself and decided to be honest from that day onwards.

5. The Boastful Lame Woman

Once, there was a boastful Lame Woman who lived in the village. One day, she left her village and travelled to the nearby town.

When the Lame Woman reached the town, she did not know anyone there. She wanted to make friends. So, she walked to the town square. There, she climbed on the raised pulpit and said, "Friends, I am new here. I want to make friends with you."

When people started gathering around her, the boastful Lame Woman thought that she would impress everyone. She said, "I am a doctor. I can cure any disease. I have medicines for all illnesses. You can come to meet me any time to cure your ailments."

Hearing this, a clever Girl said, "If you can cure everyone then why have you not cured your own leg?" All the people laughed and the Lame Woman felt ashamed as her lie was detected.

6. A Cruel Witch's Fate

Once, there lived a cruel Witch. She loved to scare little girls. She would take them to the forest and make them her slaves. One day, a Blue Fairy came to know about the cruel Witch. She decided to teach her a lesson. She bewitched the animals of the forest.

A few days later, the cruel Witch stole another Girl from her parents and brought her to the forest. However, as she was about to cross the river, an angry lion came to attack her. The Witch climbed up a tree to save her life. There, she heard the rustle of leaves behind her. She looked above and saw a large cobra between the branches of the tree. At once, she jumped into the river. But, the crocodiles of the river ate her.

Now, the Blue Fairy freed all the girls the Witch had imprisoned. They all thanked her.

7. The Three Witches

Once, there were three Witches. They troubled people and stole from them.

One day, the three Witches robbed a sack of gold from a wealthy merchant's house. Then, they all went deep into a forest, outside the town, to divide the gold amongst themselves. When they reached the forest, they felt hungry.

So, a Witch went back to the town to steal food. There, she stole from the bakery and had a tasty meal. Then, she mixed poison in two cakes for the other two Witches, because she wanted to keep all the gold.

Meanwhile, in the forest, the other two Witches were hiding behind a tree. When the first Witch arrived there, they killed her. Then, they happily sat down to eat the cakes she had brought. But, as soon as they ate them, they fell dead because of the poison.

Thus, all the Witches became victims of their evil ways.

8. The Two Maids

Joan and Sheila were maids who lived in the country. They were best friends and did all their work together.

One day, the two maids bought a barrel of milk from the dairy. "We will store this milk, so that we don't have to visit the dairy every day!" they decided.

However, as Sheila was cutting a lemon into half for lemonade, she accidentally dropped the halves in the barrel of milk. Joan said, "I will try to find it."

Thus, Joan picked a large spatula and stirred the milk to find the lemon. She stirred for a long time but could not find the pieces. "There's no point, Joan, it's all ruined!" cried Sheila. Still, Joan kept trying.

Sometime later, Joan's stirring churned the milk and it started turning into cheese! The two maids were now very happy. "See Sheila, it is good to keep trying!" said Joan.

9. Dora's Lesson

Once, there lived a young girl named Dora, who was never content with what she had.

One day, Dora found a nut. She tried to bite it but it was very hard. Her tiny teeth could not cut into it. She said, "Oh Lord! Why did you give me such tiny teeth?"

God heard Dora and said, "Dear Dora, look at other creatures. I will give you the teeth of any creature you like."

So, Dora went in search of different creatures. Finally, she saw the teeth of an Elephant. She loved the ivory white teeth of the Elephant. She said, "Wow! What beautiful teeth you have!"

At this, the Elephant said, "My teeth are just for show. I cannot use them for chewing. I simply have to bear the heavy weight of my teeth."

Dora, at once, realised her mistake and thanked God for her natural teeth.

10. Beautiful Earth

The kindergarten class of Pinkville visited the forest to enjoy a day picnic. There, one of the little girls asked their teacher, Mrs. Goodwill, "How come some places have many trees and some none, Mrs. Goodwill?"

Mrs. Goodwill replied, "When our beautiful Earth was created, there were many green fields, full of grass and trees. God also created birds and animals to live in the meadows and the fields. Finally, He created man to take care of all the beautiful creations."

"God warned the human race to be good beings; otherwise the Earth would lose all its beauty. However, when Man came to Earth, he forgot God's warning. He started stealing, lying and killing others. That is why the Earth is not as beautiful everywhere, anymore."

The kindergarten class felt very ashamed. They decided to be nice and honest people, to make the Earth a beautiful place again.

11. God's Help

Once, a rich but cowardly Woman left her city to go to another country. She undertook her journey in a ship.

On the way, a storm started to rage. The ship rocked from side to side. It collided with a rock and there was a hole in its bottom. Soon, ice-cold water started entering the ship. All the people aboard the ship started jumping into the sea to swim ashore.

Now, the rich Woman started praying, "Oh! God, please save my life!" A Man went to the Woman and said, "You should jump off the ship and try to swim ashore, like the others. See, the shore is not very far from here. God helps those who help themselves." But, the Woman did not listen. She stayed on the ship and kept praying, while all others swam safely to the shore.

Soon, the ship drowned and the Woman died.

12. The Angel of Kindness

Once, a poor Maid lived in a village. She was so poor that she could barely make ends meet. She never had enough food or clothes. Although she was leading a miserable life, she never complained.

God felt sorry for the poor Maid. "This young girl leads such a difficult life. She works so hard throughout the day. Yet, she does not have proper clothes or shelter. She has never tasted delicious food. Still, she always stays happy. She never complains and believes in me."

So, God placed a bag full of gold coins for the Maid outside her hut. Early in the morning, when she stepped outside the house, the Maid found the gold. Now she was very happy. Instead of using it for herself, she distributed it among her poor neighbours.

This made God very happy and he turned her into the Angel of Kindness.

13. Brave Olivia

Once, two sisters named Olivia and Jenna lived in the country. Their parents were rich traders. Everyone in the countryside knew that their family was extremely wealthy.

Once, two Thieves came to Olivia and Jenna's mansion. They thought, 'Ah! What a large house. Surely, its owners are very rich. We must rob it!'

The next day, when Olivia and Jenna's parents were away, the Thieves broke into their mansion and said, "Where is all the money, little girls?"

Little Jenna was very scared, but Olivia was clever. She said, "The money is kept in the bedroom — above the cupboard. I can't reach it."

As the two Thieves got into the bedroom to get the money, Olivia quickly locked the door and called her neighbours.

The neighbours beat up the Thieves and called the Sheriff, who put them in prison. Olivia's parents were very proud of their brave girl.

14. Saving Money

Sophie was a young woman who lived in the town. She was very lazy and would waste all her time. She never wished to do any work.

One day, Sophie found a bag full of money. She was very happy now. She felt that she was a lucky girl, because she found the money without any effort.

Sophie spent some money on buying sweets. Then, she bought new clothes. Thus, she started spending all the money she had found. Her friend said, "Sophie, don't waste this money. Save it for a rainy day."

But, Sophie said, "I have a lot of money. There is no need for me to save. I am so lucky; I will find more money after this!"

Slowly, Sophie spent all the money. Now she did not have a single penny. Sophie then realised that one should work hard and not believe in luck or be lazy.

15. Living in the Present

Once, there lived a Woman in the village. She always wanted to know her future. Thus, she studied astrology and the positions of Stars and Planets.

Soon, the Woman started spending all her time trying to predict her future. 'I would never be unhappy if I knew my future!' she thought.

Sometimes, she would get so engrossed with the sky that she would not even know where she was going.

One night, the Woman was walking as usual with her head up, observing the sky. She could not see the large stone in her way and tripped over it. She fell in a thorny bush. She shouted for help and a Villager helped her out.

The Villager said, "You are so busy predicting your future that you do not see what is lying in front of you!" The Woman realised her mistake and decided to live in the present.

16. Night-time Adventure

Once, a girl named Elizabeth studied at a boarding school. She was very naughty and did not like to go to bed early. Thus, every night, she would jump over the boarding school's boundary wall and wander in the night.

Elizabeth thought that no one knew of her secret. However, wise Mrs. Smith, the history teacher, knew it. She wanted to catch Elizabeth red-handed.

One night, Elizabeth sneaked out as usual. She climbed up a ladder and jumped over the wall. When she had gone, Mrs. Smith removed the ladder.

A few hours later, Elizabeth returned. She panicked when she saw that the ladder was missing. Suddenly, Mrs. Smith emerged from behind the bushes. She said, "Elizabeth, you should take a warm shawl when you wander out in the night, or you will catch a cold."

This made Elizabeth ashamed of herself. She became a sincere student after this.

17. Just One Chance

Once, there was a Thief who would cheat people for his benefit. The people of the kingdom went to their Princess for help. The Princess ordered her men to catch the Thief. He was soon caught and brought to the court.

However, the clever Thief cried and promised that he would never cheat again. The kind Princess trusted the Thief and let him go.

The Thief went away but continued to steal. Soon, he saw a rich merchant. He snatched his money and ran away. While he was running, he tripped and fell down.

The Princess' soldiers saw him. They found the stolen money in his pocket and took him to the Princess. Again, the Thief pleaded for forgiveness. But, this time, the Princess said, "I gave you one chance to mend your ways, but you wasted it. Opportunity knocks the door only once!"

Thus, she put him in prison.

18. Loving Life

Once, there lived a poor Woman in the village. She had no family. So, she was very lonely. Many a times, she would say, "Oh! I am alone. It would be better if I were dead."

Every day, the poor Woman would gather wood from the forest and sell it. She would spend all her time muttering to herself and complaining about her life.

One day, she fell sick. As she lay in bed, shivering from fever, she again started complaining, loudly. "I have no one to help me. I wish God takes me away!"

Suddenly, God appeared before her. He said, "I am here to take you with me. Come!"

Now the poor Woman was scared. She said, "Please spare my life, God! Please don't kill me! I don't want to die!"

God said, "Learn to love your life. You will realise its value when it is gone."

19. The Bitter Truth

Polka was very excited, as it was her birthday. She had invited all her friends to a party that evening. Her Mother had baked her favourite strawberry cake for her.

In the evening, Polka wore her new pink dress. She combed her hair and decorated it with ribbons.

Soon, Polka's friends started arriving. All of them wore colourful dresses and looked very beautiful. Polka was very happy, as all her friends had brought presents for her. However, Emma did not come. Polka enjoyed her party but missed Emma.

The next day, Polka met Emma and asked her why she did not come. Emma said, "Oh! I don't like parties."

Polka was angry now. She stopped talking to Emma. Then, her Mother said, "Polka, you should not be angry with Emma. She was honest with you. You should respect her nature."

Polka realised her mistake and apologised to Emma.

20. The Diamond Ring

Gia was a beautiful girl who lived in a village. One day, a jealous Witch cursed her and trapped her in the Sad World.

Now, Gia lived alone in a stone house. There was a huge field next to her house. However, the field was not green, but barren and dry. Many days passed and with each day, Gia lost all hope of escaping.

One such day, Gia saw something sparkling on her windowsill. It was a diamond ring! Gia quickly wore it. All of a sudden, the Sad World disappeared and she found herself in a beautiful castle.

A handsome Prince was standing before Gia. He said, "I wished to marry the right girl. This magical diamond ring can reach anywhere. Only the girl best suited to me could find it. I am glad that it is you!"

Soon, Gia and the Prince got married and lived happily.

21. The Queen of Fairies

Once, a Woodcutter and his Wife lived in a village. They were very sad for they did not have any children.

One day, the Woodcutter went to the forest to cut wood. On his way, he saw a Deer caught in a hunter's trap. The kind Woodcutter opened the trap and the Deer ran away.

After some days, the Woodcutter was walking in the forest, when he found a sweet little Baby girl in a basket. The Woodcutter picked up the Baby. Just then, the Deer he had saved, appeared. It soon changed into a beautiful Fairy.

The Woodcutter was very surprised!

The Fairy said, "I am the Queen of Fairies. I wander around the forest as a Deer. You saved my life. In return, I have granted your dearest wish! This baby is yours!"

The Woodcutter thanked the Fairy and ran home to his Wife with the Baby!

22. Daisy's Faith

Once, there lived a rich Merchant in a kingdom. He and his Wife had six sons and six daughters.

One night, a terrible fire burnt the Merchant's shop and storehouse. He had no money left! All his children cried, for they loved to live in luxury, but the youngest daughter, Daisy did not worry. She said, "Please believe in God. He will take care of us."

No one believed her, but still Daisy kept praying. She knew how to sew dresses, so, she started making pretty dresses from the leftover cloth they had. Soon, Daisy's dresses became very famous. The King heard of them and called Daisy to his court.

When he saw Daisy, he fell in love with her and married her. The Merchant was overjoyed as they all started living in the royal palace. He said, "Daisy, your faith saved our lives! God did take care of us!"

23. The Lost Princess

Once, a beautiful Princess was born in a kingdom. When she was ten years old, the Princess suddenly disappeared.

The King and the Queen were heartbroken. Many years passed and the King and the Queen grew old.

Then, one day, a Prince from the neighbouring kingdom visited them. The King told him about his lost daughter. The brave Prince decided to look for the Princess.

He went into the forest near the palace. There, he met an Old Lady who told him that the Elves had stolen the Princess. Then, she showed him the hidden road to the Elves' kingdom.

The Prince set off, but on his way, he met many demons and witches. He fought them all and reached the Elves' kingdom. There, he bravely fought with the Elves and brought the young Princess back to her parents.

The King was so happy that he married the Prince to the Princess.

24. June's Castle

It was a sunny afternoon. Little June was sitting in her garden and reading a book. Suddenly, she found herself in a forest. Then, she saw a huge castle at a distance. June walked towards it and climbed up a flight of stairs to the castle.

June found herself inside a main hall. The floor was covered with red carpet all over and it seemed to hold a hundred rooms! Warm fires blazed in fireplaces all around.

June spotted a door on one side of the main hall. She slowly walked through the door and saw a long dining table with many bowls, full of food! June sat comfortably on a chair and started to eat but right then, she heard her Mother calling, "June, come and have your Tea!"

June woke up with a start and laughed. She had fallen asleep and the castle and the forest were all a dream!

25. Mary and the Man

Once, a beautiful girl called Mary was unkind to people. Her parents were very angry at her behaviour. Thus, her father married her to the ugliest Man in the kingdom.

Mary was very angry but she had to go and live with him in his hut. The Man was kind to Mary, but Mary was rude to him. Time passed and Mary realised that the Man cared a lot about her.

One day, the Man was chopping wood and hurt his hand. When Mary saw him in pain, she started crying, for she loved the Man. Lo! The Man suddenly changed to a handsome Prince.

Just then, a Queen appeared before them and said, "Mary, this ugly Man is my son, the Prince. He was cursed by an evil witch and became ugly. Only true love could have rescued him. You saved my son!"

Mary and the Prince lived happily ever after.

26. The Fairy and the Pancakes

In a village, lived an old couple. They were very old and ill. They could not do much work, so the Woman made pancakes and carried them in a basket to the village market to sell them.

One day, the Woman made the pancakes and left for the market as usual. On the way, she tripped and fell on some rocks. Her knees were hurt and she could not get up. The Woman cried out in pain.

A Fairy, flying above, heard her. She came down and helped the Woman stand up. Then she touched the Woman's wounds and they were healed, at once!

The Woman gave the Fairy some pancakes. The Fairy took the pancakes to Fairyland. All the Fairies ate them. They all liked them so much that the Fairies visited the Woman's house and took the couple to live with them in Fairyland.

The couple lived comfortably in Fairyland.

27. May's Answer

Once, two sisters, Emma and May, lived on a farm.

One day, they were going to their grandmother's house across a forest. As they walked, Emma became thirsty and asked for water.

May replied, "I don't have any water!"

But Emma was very thirsty so May told her to sit on a stone, while she looked for water. May walked deep into the forest until she reached a glade, where an Elf sat on a mushroom.

The Elf said, "I can give you water but answer my question first. What is it that crawls when it's young and flies when it's big?"

May thought for a while and then smiled, "A caterpillar crawls when it is young and flies when it becomes a butterfly."

May was right, so the Elf clapped his hands and soon a jug of water appeared.

May ran to Emma with it, who drank the water, happily.

28. The Old Lady

Long ago, a Woman lived with her Daughter in a small village. They lived in a small hut. The Daughter went to the forest to collect wood, every day.

One day, she met an Old Lady, who was making beautiful statues from mud. The Daughter sat down and watched her.

Then on, the Daughter started meeting the Old Lady every day and soon, learnt to make statues from her. She made such beautiful statues that the Woman decided to present a statue to the King. She went with her Daughter to the palace.

The King fell in love with the beautiful Daughter and soon married her. Now, the Daughter became the Queen and she took her mother to live in the palace. She also went to the forest to look for the Old Lady.

She found that the Old Lady was actually a Fairy. The Fairy blessed the Queen and flew away.

29. The Elephant from Heaven

Once, there lived a girl called Sarah. Sarah's parents had died and her Uncle and Aunt were unkind to her.

One night, Sarah's Uncle asked her to sleep in the field to guard his cauliflower crop. Brave Sarah slept all alone. Then, at night, she saw that a shiny white cloud descended from the sky and an elephant stepped out from the cloud. It ate some cauliflowers and stepped into the cloud to return to the sky, but Sarah held on to its tail!

She was lifted up and after a while, she reached Heaven. She saw that the streets in Heaven were paved with silver and the palaces were made of gold. The air was filled with the fragrance of flowers and the sound of the sweet music of birds. Soon, Sarah found many other little girls like her and she lived with them, happily ever after.

30. The Fairy in the Pond

Once, there lived a Man, who had no relatives, thus, he was very sad.

The Man had a beautiful garden with a lovely pond, which was now becoming dirty. One night, he hid in the bushes and at midnight, he saw some Fairies descending from the sky. They took off their wings and put them aside. Then, they splashed each other with mud and water.

The Man quietly stole a pair of wings. When the sun was about to rise, the Fairies returned to their home in the clouds. However, the Fairy, whose wings the Man had taken away, was left behind.

The Man said to her, "I want to marry you. But if you want to go home I won't stop you." The Fairy saw that the Man was kind. She had been alone too, so she agreed to marry him. So, the two were happily married. The Man wasn't lonely any more!

1. Love for a Daughter

Once, a Man lived with his Wife and Daughter. Unfortunately, their village got flooded and the Man's Wife died in the flood.

The Man decided to leave the village and go to a town in search of work. He took his money and left with his Daughter.

On the way, Robbers attacked him. They took all his money. Suddenly, they saw the Man's little Daughter tied to his back. She looked like an angel.

They said, "If you want to save your life, give us your Daughter."

The Man fell on his knees and cried, "I don't want to live without my Daughter. So, kill me before you snatch her away."

The Robbers were deeply touched to see that the Man was ready to die for his Daughter. Then, they thought of their own daughters and how they would suffer if they died. So, they gave up stealing and went back home.

2. The Princes and the Pea

Once upon a time, there was a Prince who wanted to marry a real Princess. He travelled to faraway lands for many months and met many princesses. But, none convinced him. There was always a pinch of doubt about all of them. Troubled and sad, the Prince returned home.

One evening, there was loud thunder and lightning and rain poured down in torrents. At the same time, loud knocking was heard at the palace gates. The royal servant opened the door to find a Princess standing outside. She was drenched from head to toe and looked distressed.

The Queen thought of a plan to confirm if she was a real princess. She went to the royal guest bedroom and removed the mattress from the bed. Then, she placed a pea on the bed and covered it with 20 mattresses over which she spread twenty quilts.

The Princess had to sleep on this bed the entire night. The next morning, when the Princess woke up, the Queen asked her eagerly, "Did you sleep well last night, Princess?"

The Princess replied in a sluggish tone, "I could scarcely close my eyes. There was something hard in the bed, which was hurting me and kept me awake. Now, my body is all black and blue with pain."

The Queen immediately knew that the girl was a real Princess. Only a real princess could be sensitive and delicate enough to feel the pea hidden under twenty mattresses and twenty quilts.

The Prince was overjoyed to find a real Princess, at last. The Prince married the Princess and they lived happily in the palace.

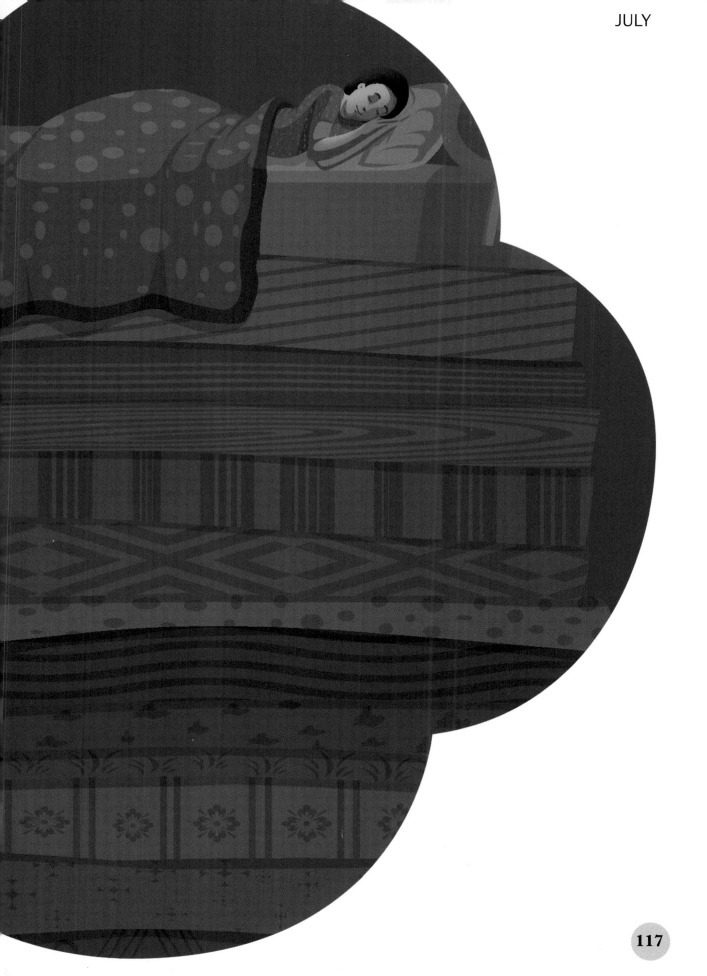

3. The Careless Girl

There once lived a Girl with her Father. She was very careless. She lost many things because of careless behaviour.

One day, her Father brought a big doll for her and said, "My dear, I bring so many things for you but you lose everything. If anything happens to this doll, I will never get any presents for you." The doll would shut her eyes while lying down and open them while standing or sitting.

The Girl promised to take care of her things but soon forgot about it. The next day, her Father came back from work and saw the doll lying in the garden. It had become wet and was spoilt. Its eyes were shut, and wouldn't open while standing or sitting!

He was very angry and took it inside. He said, "I have decided never to buy any toys for you."

The Girl started crying. She said, "Father, I am really sorry! Please forgive me!" Her Father saw that she was really sorry and forgave her.

From that day, she never lost anything. She had learnt her lesson.

4. The Clever Merchant

Once, a rich Merchant lived in a city. One day, he left his shop with precious diamonds in his suitcase. A Thief saw this and followed him.

Soon, they were caught in rain. The Merchant entered a guesthouse. The Thief followed him. But, there was only one vacant room.

So, they decided to share it. They kept their suitcases in the room and the Merchant went out for dinner.

The Thief searched his suitcase for the diamonds but did not find anything. He ran away.

After many years, the Merchant met the Thief again. The Thief asked him, "That day, I saw you take diamonds from your shop. But, I searched your suitcase and could not find anything."

The Merchant said, "I kept the diamonds in your suitcase when you went for a bath. I knew you would never search there. Fortunately, you ran away, leaving your suitcase behind!"

5. The Poor Beggar

Once, a poor Beggar went to the Village Headman. But, the Headman had gone to meet the King to ask for grants.

When the Beggar came to know about it, he thought that the King was definitely richer as he was helping the Village Headman. So, he decided to go to the King for alms.

On his way, he saw a large crowd outside a Church. When he enquired, he found that the King was praying to God to keep his treasury full all the time.

Now, the Beggar thought that God must be richer than the King.

God said, "Dear child! You should stop begging and earn your living with hard work. I promise if you work hard, you will always have enough money."

The Beggar understood and followed God's advice. Now, he worked hard and earned his living.

6. The Fifth Friend

Once, a group of five foolish Girls went for a picnic. They came across a small river on their way and decided to swim to the other side.

When they reached the other side, one Girl said, "Let us count to see if all have reached safe and nobody has drowned in the river."

The others agreed and she began the counting, "One, two, three and four! Oh! Where is our fifth friend? She is missing!"

All the Girls panicked. Then, another Girl counted and again found one girl missing. She cried out, "Our fifth friend has drowned."

All of them started crying. A passer-by enquired the reason for their sadness.

Then he made them stand in a row and counted all the five Girls. He said, "Look, you are five. All of you were counting others and leaving yourself!"

The Girls realised their foolish mistake.

7. God is Merciful

A King had a large orchard outside his palace. The Princess was very fond of fruits.

The Gardener collected ripe fruits from various trees and took them to the Princess every day.

One day, the Gardener took some cherries. The Princess was in a very bad mood that day. She picked a cherry to taste and found it sour. She threw the cherry at the Gardener in anger.

It hit the Gardener on his face, but he said, "God is merciful!" The Princess was surprised at the Gardener's words. She asked, "I have hurt you and you still say that God is merciful. Why?"

The Gardener said, "I was going to bring watermelons. But fortunately, I changed my mind. Imagine what would have happened if you had thrown a watermelon at me! So, I believe that God is merciful."

The Princess laughed at this and her anger immediately vanished.

8. How God Saved the Girl

A Witch lived on a hilltop. One day, a young Girl went to play with her brother on that hill.

The Witch was chanting to increase her powers and was disturbed by their noise. She became very angry and caught the Girl.

She said, "You have disturbed me and I will punish you."

The Girl said, "My mother says that if one hurts innocent children, God punishes him severely."

The Witch said, "God cannot harm me as I have many powers. I will burn you to ashes in a minute!"

The Girl folded her hands and prayed to God, "Dear God, save me from this evil Witch."

She opened her eyes and saw a bright light blinding the Witch's eyes. She got the opportunity to escape from her clutches and ran down the hill.

9. The Most Wonderful Doll

A poor girl, Maria, lived with her Mother and Father. One day, she saw a rich girl, Jenny, standing in a toyshop.

Jenny's Father bought her a big doll. Maria felt very sad because she did not have a single toy.

Maria's Mother said, "Don't be sad! Your Father will make you a beautiful doll, soon."

Maria's Father was a carpenter. When Maria reached home, her Mother asked her Father to make a wooden doll for her.

The next day, Maria's Father gave Maria a present. It was a beautiful wooden doll.

Maria was very unhappy, for she wanted a fancy doll like Jenny's!

Just then, she saw that her Father's hand was hurt. Maria understood that her Father had hurt his hand while making a doll for her. She, at once, went to him and said lovingly, "Father, this is the most wonderful doll ever! I love it!"

10. Faithful Mongoose

A long time ago, Mary and Tom lived on their farm with their little daughter, Sara. They had a pet Mongoose to keep away snakes.

One day, Mary went to visit her sick aunt. She left Sara behind and requested Tom to take care of her.

After a while, Tom received a message from the King's court and had to leave immediately. He left Sara in the Mongoose's care.

After some time, the Mongoose noticed a huge black snake climb on her bed.

The Mongoose immediately dragged the snake, fought with it and killed it. Tom and Mary came in the evening and saw the dead snake and Sara's room full of blood.

Then, they saw their lovely daughter play on the bed and immediately understood what that happened.

They thanked the Mongoose and kept him with them forever to take care of Sara against any dangerous animals.

11. The Ring Finger

Once, a Prince lived in a beautiful palace.

One day, he peeped inside a room from the keyhole and saw a Girl's beautiful hands. She had extremely beautiful fingers.

He decided to get married to the Girl who had such beautiful fingers. So, he ordered a diamond ring and announced, "I will marry the girl on whose ring finger this ring fits."

Princesses and beautiful girls came from different kingdoms, but none could wear the ring. The Prince was very disappointed.

He went inside his room and ordered some tea. A Maid came and served the tea to him. Suddenly, the Prince realised that she had very beautiful hands and fingers.

He put the diamond ring on her finger and it fitted her perfectly well. The Prince was extremely happy. The Maid was poor but an extremely beautiful girl.

The Prince married her soon and they lived happily ever after.

12. A Mother's Love

One day, two women came to a King's court. The first woman said, "She is my neighbour. Last night, her baby died and she stole my baby, and then kept hers in my room. Now, she denies the fact that she stole my baby."

"This baby is mine!" the second woman exclaimed.

The King's Queen was very wise. She called a guard and told him to cut the baby into half and give one half to each woman.

The first woman cried out, "Please, give the baby to the other woman, but kindly don't harm him!"

The second woman said, calmly, "Of course, you can cut him. It will solve our quarrel very well."

The Queen gave the baby to the first woman and said, "You are the real mother of the baby, for you can lose him, but not see him hurt."

Then, the Queen punished the second woman.

13. The Sun and the Moon

A long time ago, the Sun and the Moon were a married couple and lived happily on the Earth. They were best friends with the Sea and visited him every day.

One day, they decided to call the Sea for dinner. The Sea hesitated and said, "There will not be enough room for me in your house."

The Sun and Moon assured him, "We have a big house. You will not have any problem there."

So the Sea went for dinner with all the members of his family. As they entered the house, the water began to rise.

The Sun and the Moon got scared. The Sun held his lovely Moon and climbed on the roof of their house. But, the water kept rising and they finally climbed up to the sky.

Since that day, this lovely couple left the Earth. Now, they like living in the sky!

14. Equal Punishment

Once, Lisa and Dina had a fierce fight. Their friends watched silently but nobody dared to stop them.

Finally, Debby stopped them and asked, "Why are you fighting with each other?"

Lisa and Dina both started shouting and blaming the other. Debby said, "Speak one at a time, and let me hear what happened. Lisa, you speak first."

Lisa said that Dina had stolen her chocolate but Dina refused this. Debby thought for some time and said, "Everyone knows that Lisa is very clever. She can never be fooled. Thus, Lisa will be punished for falsely blaming Dina."

Dina was very happy now. But, Debby continued, "However, Dina is very greedy. So, I am sure that she is also guilty. So, both will be equally punished for fighting."

Debby taught both the girls a lesson for misbehaving. Then, she asked the others to live in peace with each other.

15. Clever Servant

Once, a Woman lived alone, far away from her family. She was a very sensitive person, and would cry easily. She also had a weak heart. Thus, any shocking news could be dangerous for her.

One day, her Servant came in. He wanted to tell her that her Mother had died, but was worried for her health.

The Servant thought of a plan and said, "Madam, I have come here to tell you that your dog is dead."

She asked, "How did that happen?"

The Servant replied, "He died due to starvation."

The Woman asked, surprised, "Why? Is my Mother not feeding them?"

Now, the Servant hugged the Woman and said, "Kind madam, your Mother died few days back. We could not tell you, since you were not well."

The Woman was very upset. But, the clever Servant had saved her life.

16. The Wise Old Lady

Once, an Old Lady lived in a village. One day, a Hermit visited her. The Old Lady served him very well. So, the Hermit gave her a magic lamp.

After the Hermit left, the Old Lady rubbed the lamp. A Genie appeared and said, "I am your slave. Give me work or I'll eat everything around me."

The Old Lady asked the Genie to grow crops in her field. The Genie completed the task quickly and came back to the Old Lady for more work.

Now, the Old Lady was worried since she did not have more work. She said, "Straighten my dog's tail. You cannot rest till you have finished this task."

The Genie tried for many days, but could not straighten the tail of the dog. He grew tired and apologised to the Old Lady. She forgave him and they lived as friends thereafter.

17. Don't Blame Others

One day, a Girl went to the beach with her Friend. She saw that a ship full of passengers hit a rock and drowned.

All the passengers in the ship died. The Girl helplessly watched this from the shore but could not do anything to save them.

In the evening, she discussed this sad event with her Friend. Her Friend said, "This is God's way of punishing bad people."

The Girl did not agree and said, "God is wrong then. To kill one bad person aboard the ship, he has killed many other innocent people."

Suddenly, a red ant bit her toe. In anger, she started stamping her feet and crushed many red ants in that area.

Seeing this, the Friend said, "Look at what you did! You killed so many innocent ants to punish the one that bit you!"

The Girl realised her mistake and apologised for blaming God.

18. Silly Fights

Once, many Girls played in a park. One day, two Girls had a fierce fight. These two Girls started gathering supporters from among the other Girls in the park.

Soon, two groups were formed. Slowly, the two groups started disliking and fighting with each other every other day.

One day, one group of Girls went to the Big Mean Girl and said, "Some Girls of the park have become our enemies. Please come to our park and trouble them." She happily agreed to do so.

Thus, the Big Mean Girl troubled the Girls of the enemy group. She even took their sweets and toys. The Girls asked her to leave the park. But, she refused, for she liked to snatch the goodies from little Girls! So, she stayed in the park and troubled all the Girls. Thus, all the Girls were hurt, because of the silly fight between two girls!

19. Lynda's Repayment

One day, Lynda was walking through a forest path. Suddenly, she saw a beautiful golden Songbird caught in a net spread by the bird catcher.

The Songbird was crying for help. Lynda ran and freed the bird. The Songbird chirped joyfully and flew away.

Some days passed. One day, Lynda was sitting on a wall and having her lunch. Suddenly, the same Songbird swooped at her food and took it away. Lynda jumped to snatch her food back, but lost her balance. She fell down the wall.

Upon recognising the Songbird, she felt very angry at the ungrateful Songbird. However, she saw a poisonous snake creeping down the wall. Now she understood that the snake must have been about to bite her while she was sitting on the wall. The Songbird had saved her from being bitten.

Lynda felt very happy with the Songbird now.

20. Spending a Penny

One day, three friends, Jenna, Sara and Farah, spotted a penny on the ground. They were very happy. They decided to buy something to eat with the penny and share it equally.

Jenna said, "I want to eat something sweet!"

Sara said, "No! I want to eat a lot of things as I am feeling hungry!"

Farah said, "No! I want to drink something, as I am thirsty!"

Thus, the three friends began fighting. As they were arguing, an Old Man passed by. He asked them why they were fighting.

Upon knowing the reason, the Old Man took the penny and bought a bunch of grapes.

Then he said, "There! Jenna, these grapes are sweet. Sara, they will ease your hunger and fruits are healthy as well! Farah, they are juicy, so they will help your thirst!"

The three friends were happy. They stopped fighting and enjoyed the grapes.

21. Lazy Gia

Gia was a poor and lazy young woman. One early morning, she saw that the Queen was out riding.

Suddenly, the Queen fell from her horse. Gia helped the Queen sit on a stone and called for her guards who were far away.

The Queen was very happy and said, "Gia, you will work for me. Come to my palace before sunset. If you are late, I will keep some other girl in your place."

Gia was very happy. She rushed home and said, "Give me lunch, Mother. Then I will go."

After lunch, Gia took a nap. In the afternoon, she went towards the palace. On the way, she felt tired. So she sat under a tree to rest.

Finally, when Gia reached the palace it was already sunset. The palace doors were shut. "I lost the Queen's offer because of my laziness! I will work properly now!" Gia promised herself mournfully.

22. The Joy of Giving

Once, there lived a poor Girl. She used to beg for food and other things.

One day, a Lady gave her some saplings instead of alms. The Girl thought, 'These saplings look very healthy. I should plant them soon, so that everyone can enjoy their fruits and flowers.'

Thus, the Girl planted the saplings by the side of her small hut. She watered them every day. A few weeks later, plenty of pretty flowers bloomed around her hut. The plants also had delicious berries. She invited little girls and old people to look at the flowers and eat the fruit.

Soon, autumn came and the flowers started falling off the plants. As the Girl went out to pick them up, she saw that they had turned into little jewels! Suddenly, an Angel appeared and said, "This is your reward for being so selfless!"

The Girl sold the jewels and built a shelter for poor homeless people.

23. Useless Pride

Jean and Kitty were two friends. Kitty made iron statues and Jean made jewellery.

One day, Jean and Kitty were going to the town with their ponies. Jean's pony had silk cloth on its back. It was carrying gold coins and precious gems in two large sacks.

Kitty's pony was simple. It was carrying some iron tools in its sacks. Jean's pony was full of pride because it was carrying precious goods. Kitty's pony was calm.

As they were passing through a forest, some Bandits stopped them. Jean and Kitty ran away, leaving their ponies behind. The Bandits searched the ponies. As they found nothing valuable on Kitty's pony, they let it go.

Then, they saw Jean's pony standing stiff with pride. They understood that it had valuable goods. And so, they carried it away with all the jewels!

24. Brave Jane

Once, there lived a girl called Jane.

One day, she went to the forest with her Father to collect wood.

Sadly, Jane got lost. Soon, night fell and she started looking for her Father.

As Jane was walking through the dark and twisted path, she found a beautiful box in the forest. It was full of gold coins!

Suddenly, a Robber appeared before Jane. He had a big sword in his hand. He said, "Give me all that you have!"

Jane gave some coins to the Robber. Then he said, "Give me the box, too!"

Jane threw the box at the Robber. It hit him on his hand and his sword fell down. Jane, at once, picked up the sword and pointed it at the Robber.

The Robber returned the coins. Just then, Jane's Father came looking for her. He hit the Robber with a stick. The Robber ran away and Jane went home with her Father, and the box of gold coins!

25. The Golden Bird

Once, a beautiful Golden Bird lived in a forest. She sang sweet and melodious songs. When she sang, shiny pearls fell from her beak.

One day, a Bird Catcher heard about the Bird. He spread his net in the forest and caught the poor Golden Bird.

The Bird Catcher took the Golden Bird home. Though he kept it in a golden cage and fed it well, the Bird was very sad. She did not sing at all and the Bird Catcher never got any pearls. Thus, he got fed up and gifted the Golden Bird to the Princess.

The Princess was a kind girl. At once, she freed the Golden Bird. The Bird was so happy that she sang aloud and a shower of pearls fell in the Princess' lap.

From that day, the Golden Bird came to meet the Princess every day to sing for her.

26. Clever Holly

Once, Holly was riding a pony. When she got tired, Holly sat under a shady tree and fell asleep. Her pony was grazing, nearby.

After a few hours, Holly woke up and saw that the pony was missing. She searched all around, but could not find her pony. She picked up a thick stick from the ground and went in search of the thief who might have stolen her pony.

Holly went to the nearby village. There she waved her stick and shouted, "Who has stolen my pony? Just keep in mind, I will do exactly what I did last time, when someone stole my pony!"

The Thief heard Holly and brought out her pony. He said, "Here is your pony. But what did you do last time, when your pony was stolen?"

Clever Holly said, "Nothing! I bought a new pony!" and walked away with her pony.

27. Fair Queen Liya

Liya was a great Queen. She was known for her sense of justice.

One day, Liya went to a riverside. She found the place very beautiful. She ordered her Prime Minister to build a palace there.

A few days later, the Prime Minister went to Queen Liya and said, "Your Highness, there is a poor old woman's hut just where the palace is to be built. It will ruin the beauty of the palace."

The Queen said, "Tell her to leave the place. In return, she will be given gold coins and a better place to live in."

The next day, the Old Woman met the Queen and begged, "I cannot leave my hut. It is my dead husband's home. I do not want a bigger house, Your Highness!"

The Queen realised the Old Woman's sentiments. So, she let the hut remain. Everyone praised her sense of justice.

28. Observant Polly

Polly was an educated but unemployed young woman. She wanted to do some work.

One day, she decided to wait for the Queen at the palace gate, and ask for a job.

Thus, the next day, Polly went to the palace gate and waited for the Queen. To pass her time, Polly started counting the people who went in through the gate. Throughout, the day, she counted ten strangers going in. By evening, only nine of them had come out.

When the Queen came out of the palace gate, Polly told her that only nine out of ten strangers had come out of the palace.

At once, the Queen ordered her soldiers to search for the stranger. He was found hiding in the Queen's chamber. He was thus caught and put in the prison.

The Queen was very happy with Polly and gave her a job as the Queen's personal companion.

29. Proud Linda

Once, a beautiful but proud girl, Linda studied in a school. She made sure that she made only pretty and rich friends.

One day, her school planned a picnic. Linda and her friends were very excited. They went for the picnic and had a lot of fun.

One of her classmates, Ben, came to her and asked, "Will you play with me?"

Linda looked at him and said scornfully, "I don't like to talk to ugly people like you."

Ben felt very bad, but did not say a word. After some time, he heard a loud shriek. He ran and saw that Linda had fallen into the lake and was drowning.

Without wasting any time, Ben jumped into the lake and saved Linda's life. All the students praised Ben, but Linda was too ashamed to say anything.

The next day, she apologised to Ben in the school and they became friends.

30. Fruits of Labour

Once, a Fisherman lived on the seashore. He caught fish and sold them in the market.

But, since a few days he had not caught any fish. He was extremely disappointed, but did not quit trying.

Finally, all his money was spent and he did not have anything to eat for days.

So, he decided, "Either I will catch a fish today or will end my life in the sea."

He went to the sea, but could not catch anything. Hungry and tired, he fell asleep in his boat.

After some time, he heard the voice of a woman and woke up. He saw a beautiful Mermaid. She said, "The Sea Goddess is very happy with your hard work."

Then, she gave him a bag full of gold coins to spend the rest of his life happily. The Fisherman was extremely happy and left for home.

31. The Dishonest Friend

Two girls, Jane and Maria grew up together and went to the same school. Jane was very pretty but Maria was ugly. She envied Jane. She never thought well for Jane. On the other hand, Jane loved Maria as a true friend.

One day, Maria forced Jane to steal apples from her neighbour's orchard. Suddenly, Maria heard the Guard coming and jumped the boundary wall to get out of the orchard.

But, Jane got locked inside. After a while, the Guard saw Maria outside and asked, "Did you see anybody enter inside?"

Mean Maria told the guard about Jane. The Guard searched, but could not find Jane! When Maria left for home, she found Jane standing outside her house.

Jane said, "I heard you and sneaked out before the Guard could find me. You are a dishonest friend. I never want to see you again!"

Mean Maria was ashamed of her dishonesty.

1. Little Tina

Once, there lived a girl named Tina. She was beautiful but short. Her friends in school teased her due to her short height.

One day, she got fed up and shouted, "I will be taller very soon."

She went home and cried all day. Her parents got worried and asked her the reason. She told them the entire story.

Her parents tried to explain, but she said, "I will not go to school till I am as tall as my friends."

A few days later, she met her Grandmother. Grandmother gave her few pills and said that they would help her grow tall.

Tina took them but instead of getting taller, her body began to itch.

Now, Grandmother gave Tina a soothing oil and explained, "You must not compare yourself with others. Else, you can land in trouble trying to achieve the impossible."

Thus, Grandmother taught Tina a good lesson.

2. The China Toys

Once, there was a little girl called Lea. She had a large mahogany cupboard in her room. A man was carved on the cupboard. He had the legs of a goat, and looked very scary.

Lea had three toys made of china. One was a pretty young Girl. The other was a handsome Man and the third toy was an Old Man.

The Girl and the Man wanted to get married. And, the Old Man was the Girl's Grandfather. One day, the Cupboard Man said to the Old Man, "I am made of mahogany. I am strong and beautiful. Let me marry your granddaughter!"

The Old Man said, "Yes, I shall marry my granddaughter to you."

Hearing this, the Girl got very sad. She said to her lover, "Let us leave this room and live outside! I do not want to marry the scary Cupboard Man!" The Man agreed to do so. Soon, the two china toys carefully climbed up the chimney, and sat on the top of the roof.

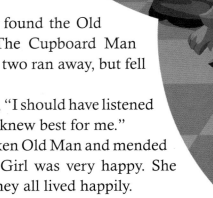

Now, the Girl saw a huge world, with people, animals and trees. She felt very scared. She said to the Man, "I am very scared, dear one! Please take me back to the room." And so, the Man took her back inside the room through the chimney.

However, the two china toys found the Old Man broken inside the room. The Cupboard Man said, "He tried to stop you as you two ran away, but fell down and broke."

The Girl began to cry and said, "I should have listened to Grandfather. He was wise and knew best for me."

The next day, Lea saw the broken Old Man and mended him with cement and glue. The Girl was very happy. She listened to her Grandfather and they all lived happily.

3. The Naughty Girl and the Huge Man

Once, a naughty Girl lived in a village. She broke pots, made cattle run away and added lots of salt in food to purposely trouble others.

She caused trouble in the entire village. People were fed up and decided to teach her a lesson.

One day, the Girl was playing. A few men went to her and said, "A huge man lives on the hill top. He sleeps all day. If you wake him, we will give you gold."

The Girl was very happy. She agreed and went on the hill top.

There, she saw a huge man sleeping. She tickled him by putting pieces of grass in his ear and nose. The Man got up. He caught hold of the Girl and shouted, "How dare you wake me up?"

The Girl was terrified and wanted to run. But, the Man kept her as a slave to teach her a lesson.

4. The Boatman's Daughter

Long ago, a proud Priest lived in a village. He boasted a lot about his intelligence.

One day, he went to a Boatman and said, "Take me in your boat to the nearby village."

The Boatman said, "Sir, I am not well today."

The Priest screamed, "I do not care. Send your Daughter to row the boat."

The Boatman's Daughter agreed. On the way, the Priest said, "Oh! You don't know how to row a boat. Your life is worthless!"

When the Daughter asked him for the fare of the boat, the Priest refused to pay.

Now, the Daughter got very upset. She took the boat in deep waters and rocked it. The Priest fell in the water and began to drown.

She said, "Oh! You know so much. Don't you know how to swim?"

Then she rescued the Priest and said, "One should not consider anybody inferior."

The Priest learnt his lesson.

5. The Woman Who Tried to Fool God

Once, a rich and greedy Woman fell ill. Many doctors tried to cure her but were not successful.

Finally, she prayed to God, "God, please save me from death. If you do so, I will get a beautiful temple built for you."

God heard the prayers and she was cured.

Now, she did not want to spend much money. So, she got a tiny idol of God made and took it to the nearby temple. Then, she said, "God, please accept my gift of thanks."

God got very angry because she had broken her promise. He decided to punish her.

He came in her dream that night and said, "Go to the sea shore and you will find a bag full of gold coins."

The greedy Woman immediately got up and ran all the way to the sea. Soon, she got tired, fell down on the way, and was never heard of again.

6. Lazy Friends

Many years ago, two friends, Lizzy and Maria lived in the same house. Both of them were very lazy.

Each waited for the other to finish the household work, but nobody did it. So, the entire house looked like a mess.

Slowly, rats, mosquitoes and other insects gathered in their house and spread diseases.

Soon, both the friends fell ill. They called the Doctor. He was shocked to see the state of the house.

While he was examining Lizzy and Maria, they said, "Please give us medicines that prevent us from falling sick again."

The Doctor looked at them, angrily, and said, "You have fallen sick due to your own laziness. If you would have been little careful and had kept your house clean, you could have avoided these diseases."

Lizzy and Maria were ashamed of their laziness. They decided to be careful and keep their surroundings clean in the future.

7. Intelligent Princess

Long ago, a Princess lived in a magnificent palace. She was famous for her kindness.

One day, she noticed a Beggar rubbing his back against the gates of the palace. She asked, "Why are you rubbing your back against our gate?"

He replied, "I am poor and have not had a bath for days. So, my back is itching." The Princess pitied him and gave him twenty gold coins.

This news spread through the kingdom.

A few days later, the Princess saw two Beggars rubbing their backs against the gates. She ordered, "Give these Beggars twenty whiplashes to cure the itch."

They cried, "You gave the other Beggar twenty gold coins. Why are you punishing us?"

The Princess replied, "He was alone, so he could not scratch his own back. But you both can scratch each other's backs and are here because of greed."

The two Beggars felt really ashamed.

8. Tit for Tat

Once, a little Girl went out to play in the evening. On the way, she saw an Ice Cream Seller.

He had a lovely red cart with pictures of mouth-watering desserts. He called to attract children, "Strawberry, vanilla, chocolate and butterscotch... Come and take any of them!"

The Girl went near the cart. She searched her pockets for money, but only found a few nuts.

The Seller saw the nuts and thought, 'I should fool the Girl and give her an old and useless ice-cream in exchange of the nuts.'

He made the offer to the Girl and she agreed. He gave her the oldest orange bar and took the nuts.

After the Girl walked away with the ice cream, the Seller started eating the nuts in peace. As he ate, he realised that all of them were rotten. He was disappointed but understood God's way of 'Tit for Tat'!

9. Clever Queen

Long ago, a Queen lived in her magnificent palace. She was kind and loved by all.

One day, she received a dinner invitation from a wicked King. Her ministers advised her to decline the invitation.

She thought for a while and said, "The King will think that I am a coward if I don't go. So, I will certainly go."

The next day, the King waited for her. He ordered his soldiers to put the Queen in the prison as soon as she reached, without meeting her.

Then, he rested in peace. After a while, his guards informed him, "The neighbouring kingdom has attacked us. Their Queen cleverly sent her maid to judge your intentions."

The King prepared to fight the battle. But, the Queen had already conquered his palace by then. She put him in prison and freed many kings and princes.

All praised the Queen for her cleverness.

10. Pride Invites Trouble

Once, a Banyan and a Mango tree grew on the roadside. The Mango tree bore sweet and juicy mangoes.

Many people would rest under it and enjoy its sweet fruits. But none paid attention to the old Banyan tree.

Slowly, the Mango tree grew proud. One day, it said, "Old Banyan, I am very important. Everyone likes my tasty fruits. People nourish me with water. But nobody bothers about you."

The Banyan tree said, "Don't be so proud! Everything has its own advantages and disadvantages."

The next day, some boys picked all the mangoes from the Mango tree. They broke many branches and leaves, too. After that, the Mango tree looked very ugly.

Now, the Banyan tree said, "Your lovely mangoes were advantageous for you but today they invited so much trouble. You have got hurt while I stand completely safe here. So, one should never be proud."

11. The Riddle

Once, a Queen wanted to appoint a Prime Minister. She announced, "I have a riddle. Whosoever will solve it would be my Prime Minister."

Then, she said, "A man has a goat, a lion and a bundle of grass. The man has to cross a river and take the three to the other bank in such a way that no one will eat the other. Also only two can go in a boat at one time. How will he do it?"

Many people tried to solve the riddle, but failed.

Then, a young Woman said, "First, the man will take the goat. Then, he will go to get the lion. He will bring the lion to the other bank and take the goat with him. Then, he would leave the grass with the lion and row back to get the goat."

The Queen was impressed with her intelligence and appointed her as the Prime Minister.

12. The Son of God

Once, a Man lived in a village. He was extremely hard working and earned a lot of wealth. But, he did not believe in God.

After some time, he married a beautiful Girl. She was very religious and prayed to God every day.

The Man could never understand her prayers and got upset. One day, they had an argument. The Man said, "Who is God? Where is he? If he is around us, tell him to prove his presence. I challenge him to kill me."

An Old Man of the village heard them fight and stopped by. He said, "Dear son, will you kill your son if he asks you to do so? God is also like your father. He can never harm you. You must have faith in him."

The Man was ashamed and apologised to his wife. After this, he also prayed to God every day and remained peaceful.

13. Forgetful Lisa

Once, a girl named Lisa lived in a town. She went to a good school and had many friends.

However, Lisa had one bad habit. Whenever, she did not want to do something, she would say, "I forgot!"

One day, her friend Marilyn requested, "You have my notebook. Please get it tomorrow, or else the Teacher will scold me."

Lisa was angry with Marilyn for some reason and purposely did not get the notebook. When Marilyn asked, she said, "Oh! I completely forgot."

Marilyn was extremely upset and decided to teach her a lesson. She involved the other students in the plan.

The next day, the entire class went for a picnic. While coming back, everybody left Lisa at the picnic spot. She wandered alone and reached home with great difficulty.

Later, she complained to her friends. All of them shouted together, "Oh! We forgot!" Now, Lisa understood and realised her mistake.

14. Free Coconut

Once, a miserly Old Woman lived in a village.

One day, she went to buy a coconut and asked its price. The Shopkeeper said, "Ten copper coins each!"

The Woman said, "I will not pay more than five copper coins for this."

So, the Shopkeeper advised her to go to another market. The Woman walked five miles and reached the other market.

There, the Shopkeeper agreed to give her a coconut for five coins, but now she wanted it for three coins.

Then, she was advised to go to the seashore. She walked three miles to reach the shore. The Coconut Seller agreed to sell it to her for three coins, but she refused.

She looked at the tree and decided to climb it and pick a coconut for free. She tried, but her foot slipped and she broke her leg.

Now, she had to pay thousand coins to the doctor!

15. The Kind Woman

Many years ago, a Queen and her army fought a long battle. After the victory, they decided to return to the palace.

On the way, their food got finished. Now, everybody was very hungry. So, the Queen ordered, "Minister, go to the largest farm and get all the fruits."

The Minister stopped a Woman and said, "Take me to the largest farm to pick fruits."

The Woman led him to a farm. The Minister and other soldiers picked all the fruits available there. Then, the Minister asked, "Is this the largest farm?"

The Woman replied, "No, this is my farm. I could not take you to somebody else's property knowing that you will pick all that is there."

The Minister was touched and praised the Woman's generosity in front of the Queen. The Queen rewarded her with two big farms to spend the rest of her life happily.

16. The Intelligent Painter

Old and wealthy Margaret lived with her Dog. She loved her Dog. One day, she decided to get her portrait made and went to a Painter.

The Painter agreed. A week later, Margaret came with her Dog to collect the portrait. She waited for her Dog's reaction on seeing the portrait.

The Dog turned his face and refused to look at it. Margaret was very disappointed and shouted, "You have made a horrible thing. Even my Dog refuses to look at it. I will not pay you a penny for this."

The Painter requested her for a last chance. Margaret agreed and came three days later with her Dog.

Now, the Dog immediately started licking the portrait. Actually, the Painter had rubbed a piece of meat on the portrait.

Margaret thought that the Dog liked her portrait and paid a lot of money to the Painter happily!

17. Silly Catherine

Once, there lived a girl named Catherine. She was very foolish and did not use her brain at all.

One day, Catherine went for a walk in the forest. Soon, she got tired of walking. She sat under a tree and fell asleep.

When Catherine woke up, it was dark. She decided to go home. As she was walking, she came across a lake. 'Let me drink some water!' thought Catherine. However, when she bent to drink from the lake, she could not see her reflection in the water. This was because it was very dark.

So Catherine thought she was invisible! She walked in front of a monkey fearlessly, for she thought it could not see her. However, the monkey could see her! It jumped at her and scratched her all over.

Silly Catherine was taught a lesson for not using her brain.

18. The Monitor

Once, there was an obedient and responsible girl called Pam.

Pam's class was going for a picnic to the city park in their school bus.

The Teacher called Pam and said, "Pam, you will be the monitor, today. You have to take care that no one puts their hand or head out of the bus window. Also, make sure we don't miss anyone."

Pam replied, "I will do so, Teacher."

The girls boarded the bus and went to the park. They played games there and ate their snacks.

Finally, it was time to go back. As the bus was ready to go, the Teacher noticed Pam peeking out of the bus window. She said, "Pam, why are you peeking out? I thought you were a responsible girl!"

Pam said, "Madam, I was checking if anyone is left behind."

The Teacher was happy that Pam did her job well.

19. Bossy Paula

Five-year-old Paula was an adorable little girl. However, she was very bossy and would always order her friends.

One evening, Paula went to the park. Her friends were playing Doctor and Patients. Paula said, "I want to play Teacher. I will be the teacher. Jenna, you will be the student. Lea will be the peon and Belle will be the school bus driver."

Paula's friends were tired of following her orders. Together, they said, "No! All of us want to play Doctor. Don't order us around!"

Paula ran home in tears. Her Mother asked, "How come you are back so early, Paula?"

Sobbing, Paula told her about her friends and said, "They are mean girls, Mother!"

Mother said, "Paula, they are right. You should not force them to play the games of your choice. You should all play peacefully."

Paula realised her mistake and decided not to be bossy.

20. Lazy Penny

Penny was a lazy girl who disliked working hard. An Angel decided to teach her a lesson.

The Angel appeared in Penny's house and said, "Penny, go to the end of the rainbow. You will find treasure, there."

Penny was very happy now. However, she did not know which end of the rainbow to go to. Finally, she went to the left end. There was nothing there.

Now, Penny was very angry. She began walking towards the right end. It was a long, twisted path. Penny reached there, feeling very tired. There, she saw the Angel. She angrily said, "You did not tell me which end to go to!"

The Angel said, "My dear, whichever end you travelled to first, you would not have found anything. I wanted to make you work hard." Then, the Angel gave her the treasure.

Now, Penny understood that treasure only came through hard work.

21. The Mirror

Belle was a pretty girl who lived in the village. She would help the poor, teach the children and read to the old.

Once, a White Fairy visited the village. She saw Belle and observed how helpful she was. The White Fairy decided to test her and bewitched Belle's Mirror.

When Belle saw her reflection in the Mirror, she screamed in terror. She looked very frightening now! Her pretty face was large and swollen, her blue eyes were now red and her nose was a pig-like snout.

The Mirror said, "I shall turn your face pretty, again, only if you promise to be rude and cruel to everyone."

But, Belle said, "No! I shall live with this ugly face, but will not stop helping my people."

Suddenly, the Mirror shattered and the White Fairy appeared, smiling. She said, "Dear Belle, you have passed my test!" and gave Belle magical healing powers.

22. The Foolish Friends

Once, a Fairy appeared before two poor friends, Janice and Mona. The Fairy said, "You have worked very hard for so many years. I am very happy with you. You can ask for any three wishes and they shall be granted."

Janice and Mona happily said, "Thank you! We will think about what we want and then tell you."

That night, they sat in their little hut, thinking of three wishes. Suddenly, Mona said, "I wish, we had chicken to eat." At that moment, a chicken appeared on the plate.

Janice scolded her, "Foolish girl, you have wasted a wish! I hope this chicken sticks to your nose!"

As she said so, the chicken flew and stuck to Mona's nose. The two friends were scared now. Mona quickly said, "I wish to be free of this chicken."

Thus, the chicken vanished. All three wishes were wasted because the foolish friends spoke without thinking.

23. Clever Gabrielle

Once, there was a kingdom named Azure. A wise and just Queen ruled it.

Gabrielle was the Queen's royal jester. She was very clever. She cracked very funny jokes and also helped the Queen in matters of the State. Many a times, Gabrielle would even crack jokes at the Queen!

One day, the Queen felt insulted at one of Gabrielle's jokes. She grew very angry and said, "Guards, seize this woman! Put her in prison. She will be hanged, tomorrow!"

The next morning, Gabrielle was brought to the court. The Queen asked, "You are going to be hanged, soon. What is your last wish?"

Clever Gabrielle replied, "Your Majesty, I wish to die of old age."

The Queen began laughing at Gabrielle's wit. She forgot her anger and said, "You are indeed the cleverest jester ever! From now on, I promise to take your jokes in good humour."

24. The Cruel Lady's Fate

Once, there lived an Old Woman. She would beg alms from the villagers, every day. Even though she was poor, she was very generous and would share with the needy.

One day, the Old Woman reached a rich Cruel Lady's house. The Cruel Lady rudely said, "I don't have anything for you!"

The Old Woman said, "Please help me, for I am poor." So, the Cruel Lady angrily went inside. She mixed poison in some leftover food and gave it to her.

The Old Woman took the food to the riverside. As she was about to eat, a little Boy came and said, "I am hungry."

The Old Woman gave all the food to the Boy. But, she was shocked when he ate the food and became very sick.

Later, she found out that the little Boy was the Cruel Lady's son. The Cruel Lady's evil deeds had resulted in the poisoning of her own son!

25. The Stubborn Woman

Once, there lived a young Woman. She had a beautiful house in the mountains, a loving Husband and a lot of wealth. Still, she was very sad. The reason behind it was that she had no child.

The Woman started praying, every day. She would pray day and night, for hours, in the hope of getting a son.

A few months later, God appeared before her and said, "What do you want, my child?"

"O God, I want a son!" the Woman said.

God said, "I can grant you a daughter. Is that fine?"

"No! I only want a son!" said the Woman. God said, "I will grant you a son, but your stubbornness will bring you pain."

Soon, the Woman had a son. But, the Boy grew disobedient and dishonest. He earned bad name for the Woman. Now she realised that she was being punished for her stubbornness.

26. Careless Jenna

Jenna was a rich but foolish girl. She would trust strangers and was careless with her money.

One day, Jenna visited the town. There, she saw a café. It was warm and beautiful. It smelled of delicious coffee. Jenna decided to buy the café.

She asked a Man, nearby, "Excuse me, sir. I want to buy this café in a hundred gold coins. Where can I find the owner?"

The Man said, "I am the owner. Give me the gold and the café is yours." Thus, he took the money and went away.

Jenna happily walked inside the café and said to the waiters, "Kind fellows, I am the new owner of this café."

A Lady said, "Says who? This café is mine!"

Jenna was taken aback. Now she realised that the Man was a liar and had duped her. She decided to be careful with strangers from that day on.

27. False Bravery

Many people tell brave tales about themselves, but are very scared in dangerous situations.

Kelly was one such woman. One day, she told her friends, "Tomorrow, I shall go to the forest and hunt a bear."

Her friends got excited and said, "Brave Kelly, please take us along!"

Kelly agreed. The next day, she and her friends went to the forest. Kelly was leading the way. As they walked through the forest, they met a Woodcutter. Kelly asked, "My good man, have you seen the footprints of a bear?"

"Yes, I have seen them," said the Woodcutter, putting down his axe, "and I will take you to its den."

Kelly went pale with fear and started to tremble. "Thank you, but that will not be necessary!" she stammered. "I am just looking for tracks, not for the bear!"

Now Kelly's friends knew that she had been lying about her bravery.

28. Working Hard

Once, there lived a hard working Farmer. He had two farmhands, Cleo and Rio. Cleo took care of sowing the crops and Rio took care of the stored grains.

One day, the Man asked Cleo, "How is the work going?"

"I need water to irrigate the land. I hope that it rains hard!" replied Cleo.

Then, the Man went to Rio and asked the same question. He said, "I pray for dry weather so the stored grains don't get damp!"

Now the Man was in despair, for both his farmhands wanted opposite weathers. Suddenly, the Angel of Kindness appeared before him and said, "You are a hard working Man. Don't be sad!"

The next morning, Cleo and Rio came running and were both very happy. On being questioned, they told the farmer that Rio had sent all the grain to the market last afternoon when the Sun shone bright. And the night saw a gentle rain that had watered the growing crops!

29. Pansy and Rose

Two girls, Pansy and Rose lived in an orphanage. They were best friends.

One day, two different families adopted them. And so, they had to go and live in two different towns. The girls exchanged their pendants and promised to find each other when they grew up.

Now, Pansy's foster parents were very kind and loved her a lot. But, poor Rose's parents were mean and made her do all the housework.

Many years passed and the girls grew up.

One day, Rose was selling vegetables in the market. Suddenly, a beautiful girl in a lovely dress stopped by her. She stared at Rose's pendant for a while and said, "Rose, is that you? I am Pansy, your friend. I have been looking for you."

Rose was so happy that she started crying. Pansy hugged her and took her home with her. They lived together, happily ever after.

30. Elaine's True Love

Once, a young girl called Elaine lived in a village. Elaine dearly loved Lance, who was her neighbour. However, Lance loved Rosaline.

Elaine was sad but wished Lance well.

Then, one day, Rosaline asked Lance to bring her a wild flower from the nearby forest. Lance readily agreed. But, in the forest, a wild boar hurt him, quite seriously.

When Elaine heard about it, she went to his house and took care of Lance. Soon, Lance was better. He thanked Elaine and went to meet Rosaline. She asked him if he had brought the wild flower.

Lance was amazed for Rosaline did not care how unwell he had been; she just wanted her flower. Lance, then thought of Elaine and how kind she had been. He went to her and said, "Elaine, your love is truly pure. It has made me love you, dearly, too."

Soon, they both were happily married.

31. The Beggar Girl

Maria studied in the local school. Every day, she noticed a poor beggar girl standing outside her school. She always went to talk to the girl, but the girl ran away, as if scared.

Then, for a few days, Maria did not see the girl at all. One evening, Maria was going to a circus with her parents. On the main road, she saw the girl again. Maria ran to her and asked her what she was doing there. The girl said that she lived with her ill mother and was begging for money to buy her mother's medicine.

Maria's parents were very kind. They, at once, took the girl's mother to a hospital. Then, they took the girl home with them.

When the girl's mother was well, she started working in Maria's house. And so, the girl started living with Maria and went to school with her every day.

1. Ricardo

In a faraway town, a girl lived with her family. Her parents named her 'Ricardo'.

One day, the Teacher said, "I wonder why your parents gave you a boy's name!" Then, all her friends teased her.

That day, Ricardo cried all day. Her parents tried to explain, but she did not listen. She wanted to change her name, immediately.

The next day, Ricardo's Grandmother came to visit. She went to Ricardo's room and asked, "Dear child, my name is Juvenile. It means 'young'. Am I young?"

Ricardo replied, "No, you are really old."

Grandmother smiled and said, "If my name's meaning cannot make me young then how can your name make you a boy? You were named after your brave Grandfather. So, whenever you think of your name, think that you have to be brave and fight for your country like he did."

Ricardo understood. She hugged her Grandmother and thanked her.

2. The Elfin Hill

Once, there was a city called the Elfin Hill. The King of Elfin Hill had two daughters. He wanted his daughters to get married. So, he invited his old friend, the Goblin King, to his kingdom for a feast.

The Goblin King had two sons. He also wanted his sons to get married, and he readily accepted the Elf King's invitation.

The day of the feast arrived. The people of Elfin Hill decorated the castle with colourful hangings and beautiful flowers. The kitchen elves cooked a delicious feast.

Soon, the Goblin King arrived with his two sons. As they were having dinner, the eldest daughter said, "I am an excellent dancer!"

The Goblin King replied, "Bah! How will your dance be useful in household work? I shall not marry my son to you."

The next daughter said, "I can make things vanish!"

The Goblin King said, "What? I do not like that. I am sure that my son will also not like this! No, you will not make a good wife."

Now, the Elf King felt very sad, for the Goblin King had rejected his daughters. However, the Goblin King's older son said, "Father! I like the oldest daughter's dance. I want to marry her!"

Then, the second son said, "And I find the second daughter interesting! She can make objects vanish! I want to marry her!"

The sons together said, "Father, we shall always come to you to gain wisdom, for you are older and learned. However, we can also make the right decisions ourselves!"

Now, the Goblin King realised his mistake. He said, "O my sons! I should have asked for your choice. I shall let you make your own decisions now."

And then, the Goblin King's sons were married to the Elf King's daughters. Everybody celebrated the wedding!

3. The Crooked Tree

Once, a big forest had many beautiful trees like Mango, Teak and Oak and many beautiful plants and flowers.

But, there was also a Crooked Tree in the forest. He was ugly and had grown very old.

The beautiful trees did not like him. They teased him and said, "You spoil the beauty of the entire forest. All the other trees are young with lovely leaves and flowers, but you look extremely ugly."

The Crooked Tree felt hurt, but kept quiet.

One day, the Queen sent her Men in the forest to gather wood to make new carriages and furniture for the palace.

The Queen's Men cut all the trees for wood. When they came to the Crooked Tree, they thought, 'The wood of this tree would not be any good to us. Let's not cut it.'

The Crooked Tree thanked God for making him crooked. It saved his life!

4. Tracy

Once, a girl named Tracy studied in a school. Her friends loved her, but were upset because of her one bad habit. She had a lot of money, but never spent it. Rather, she made her friends spend money on her whenever they went out.

One day, Tracy's friends decided to teach her a lesson. They decided to go to the ice cream parlour after school.

There, they had as many ice creams as they could. Tracy also ate two sundaes thinking that her friends would pay the money as usual.

After finishing the ice creams, all the friends left without paying the bill. Now, Tracy had to pay the entire bill!

Next day, she asked her friends, "Why did you leave the parlour without paying your bills?"

The friends asked, "Do you remember the times we paid on your behalf?"

Tracy realised her mistake and was ashamed.

5. How Lillian Remembered God

Lillian, a girl of fourteen, was suffering from an incurable disease. Her cousin, Kate came to stay with her for a while.

Kate knew that Lillian would die soon. So, she read stories of fairies and unicorns for her and asked Lillian to listen carefully.

But, Lillian did not bother. Instead, she liked to play with orphans in an orphanage. She made her mother bake cakes for them.

Slowly, Lillian donated all her toys to them. Kate did not like it and said, "Lillian, you have a few days to live. You should listen to stories and pray to God instead of wasting your time with these children."

Lillian smiled and said, "Everyone has their own way to remember God. God says, 'We must help the poor and needy.' So, I want to practise what God preaches, rather than only listen to it."

Kate agreed with her cousin and helped her pass her last days happily.

6. Way to God

Once, there was a church in a village. People came and prayed there on Sundays.

The Father was a noble man and showed all the people 'the way to God.'

A young woman, Lily, came to church every Sunday. After the prayers, she talked to the Father for long hours and discussed various religious issues.

Lily told Father, "I pray regularly to God. I do a lot of charity and show all people the right path."

One day, the Father decided to test her. He asked a Beggar to beg from Lily.

The Beggar asked Lily for some food. She did not bother and entered the church. The Beggar followed her and begged again.

Lily got irritated and asked the Beggar to leave her alone, and get out of the church.

Now, the Father came out and said, "Lily, you can never reach God if you are cruel to others."

Lily was ashamed.

7. Brave May

A little girl, May lived with her parents and her little sister, Susan.

One day, May decided to go for a walk over the bridge. Susan also wanted to go but her Mother refused, as she was very naughty.

Susan started crying. So, May requested her Mother, "Do not worry! I'll take care of her."

The Mother was hesitant but agreed. Happily, the two sisters started walking to the park through the bridge. But, naughty Susan left her sister's hand as soon as she reached over the bridge. May ran behind her.

Suddenly, Susan's foot slipped and she was about to fall into the river. But, May ran just in time and grabbed her hand. Susan was saved but May was badly hurt. She had bruises all over. Some people, who were passing by, carried both the sisters home and told the parents about May's bravery.

The parents kissed and thanked May for saving Susan's life.

8. Jenny Saves a Life

Jenny lived with her parents in a lovely house. Jenny's parents were very religious and taught her to always help others.

During the summer holidays, Jenny's Aunt and her two-year-old cousin, Will, came to stay with them for a few days.

One day, Jenny's Mother and Aunt went to the market and left Will in Jenny's care. Soon, Will fell asleep and Jenny went into the garden to water the plants.

A little while later, she noticed smoke coming out of Will's room. She ran in and saw that the carpet had caught fire from the fireplace.

Will was standing on the bed and shouting. Jenny was scared and wanted to run and save herself, but was reminded of her Mother's words, "One must always help others."

She ran and piled all the blankets that she could get, on the fire to extinguish it. Then, she picked Will up and took him downstairs.

Her parents and Aunt praised her for saving Will's life.

9. The Proud Girl

There was once a very proud girl named Elizabeth. She always asked silly questions and teased people for not answering.

Her friends came up with a plan to put an end to her questions.

They gathered all of Elizabeth's classmates and friends. Abbey, her classmate, went up to Elizabeth and said, "We have three questions for you. If you do not answer them correctly, you can never ever question any of us."

Elizabeth thought she always knew the answers to all questions. She immediately agreed to the deal.

Abbey asked, "Who runs faster than the wind? What is the best help in trouble? Which is the sweetest thing in the world?"

Elizabeth did not know the answers. She was embarrassed. Abbey said, "Your heart runs faster than the wind. Support is the best help in trouble. Polite words are sweetest in the world."

Elizabeth promised never to ask silly questions or make fun of her friends.

10. The Bigger Fool

Once, a young girl named Robin wanted to buy a diamond ring. She went to a shop and found a ring that she liked. She asked the shopkeeper for the cost of the ring. The shopkeeper said, "It costs two hundred gold coins."

Robin said, "That is too costly. I want that ring for a hundred gold coins." But the shopkeeper refused.

Robin thought the shopkeeper would give it to him for a hundred gold coins, if she came back later. So she returned that evening.

She asked the shopkeeper, "Will you give me that ring for a hundred gold coins?"

"Sorry," said the shopkeeper, "I have already sold that ring for five hundred gold coins."

"You are a fool!" said an angry Robin. "That ring must be worth five thousand gold coins. You sold it for only five hundred gold coins."

The shopkeeper said, "You missed it. You did not buy it for two hundred gold coins this morning. You are a bigger fool than I am."

11. Joseph's Wife

Joseph and his Wife were poor. Joseph had some bad friends.

One day, Joseph came home with some friends. His Wife was angry because the friends ate all the food they had. So Joseph went to the store to buy some more bread.

Meanwhile, his friends saw a decorated cane and asked Joseph's Wife about it. She said, "Joseph considers this as God. Once, you've eaten, he will beat you all with this."

His friends got scared and ran away. On his way back, Joseph saw them running away. He asked his Wife what had happened.

She said, "They wanted this cane and I refused to give it. So, they ran away."

Joseph said, "I will give it to them." He ran after them with the cane. His friends thought that he was coming to beat them. They ran faster!

Joseph's friends never came to his house any more. His Wife was happy now.

12. Eve's Plan

Eve's Father was a great warrior. Once, he sent Eve to the market to buy a new horse.

When Eve was passing through the jungle, some Thieves stopped her. "We will kill you if you don't hand over all your money now!" said one.

Eve said, "You can try. I am not scared because a fortune-teller has told me that only blind men can kill me. I see that you all are not blind."

On hearing this, the Thieves blindfolded their eyes and acted like blind men. Immediately, Eve ran away from them.

The Thieves understood Eve's plan. They were angry and started chasing her.

Eve reached the highway and saw the Sheriff. She stopped the Sheriff and explained to him all about the blindfolded Thieves.

The Sheriff caught the Thieves and punished them.

The Sheriff appreciated Eve for her presence of mind and rewarded her with a medal.

13. The Clever Reply

Once, there lived a clever poetess named Misha. She told the Queen, "I dreamt that you are the Queen of Queens. My dream will come true."

The Queen was very happy and gave Misha a hundred gold coins.

One her way home, one coin slipped and fell in a hole. Misha started looking for it.

In the evening, the Queen saw Misha on the road and asked her what she was doing. Misha replied, "I lost one of the coins and am not able to find it."

The Queen said, "You are very greedy. You were looking all day for just one coin when you have ninety-nine more."

Misha said, "Your Majesty, I am not greedy. I wanted to save that coin because it was a gift from you. Royal gifts cannot be ignored like that."

The Queen was very happy and gave Misha another bag of gold coins!

14. The Unbreakable Pots

Ruth lived in a village. She made beautiful clay pots. People loved her clay pots and bought them. But, they complained that they broke easily. Soon, Ruth got tired of hearing this.

One day, Ruth prayed to God to grant her a wish. When God appeared before her, she asked, "My customers are very unhappy about my pots. Could you please make them unbreakable?"

God said, "I shall grant your wish. The pots you make will never break." Ruth was very happy.

Ruth's pots never broke now. Thus, people did not have to buy new ones. Ruth was not able to sell any more pots! This made her sad.

So, she prayed to God again. When God appeared, she said, "Please make my pots like they were before. I will be happy with what I have, from now."

God was happy that Ruth had learned her lesson. He granted her wish.

15. The Lazy Princess

Once, there was a very lazy Princess. She never exercised. She ate and slept all day. Soon, she fell sick. The Queen called the Royal Doctor to see her.

The Doctor knew that the Princess' problem was her laziness. But it would be very rude to tell her that. So, the Doctor made a plan.

He gave the Princess a skipping rope and said, "This is magical. Skip with it for half an hour in the morning and half an hour in the evening. You will feel better soon."

The Princess did not know that it was an exercise. Thinking that it was a treatment, she followed it regularly.

Within a few days, the Princess became very healthy and fit.

She asked the Royal Doctor, "How did the magic work?"

The Doctor said, "It is not magic. You need to exercise your body regularly and you will never fall ill again."

16. The Golden Roof

Holly was a poor little girl. She lived in a small house.

One day, Holly was sitting in her yard. She saw a beautiful house with a golden roof on the other side of the hill. She wished she lived in the golden house.

Holly wanted to take a closer look at the house. So, she walked towards that house to see it. As she got closer, the glittery roof slowly disappeared. It was just a normal roof.

Holly was very disappointed and surprised to see this. She turned to go back home. Then, she noticed that the roof of her house was shining as if it was made of gold. Holly was amazed at this.

Then she understood that the roof was shining because of the sun's golden rays falling on it.

Holly realised that our eyes make something beautiful or ugly, hence, we should look at everything positively.

17. The World is Round

One day, Mary was crossing a river. The shoe from her left foot fell into the water. Mary was very sad, as now her mother would get angry and even punish her. She went home, unhappy.

A man who was fishing caught Mary's shoe instead of a fish. He left it on the bank of the river.

A Pigeon scooped the shoe from the bank and flew away with it. On the way, the shoe slipped from the Pigeon's beak. It landed in a garden where some people were having a picnic. A little boy picked up the shoe and threw it over the fence into a cowshed.

The shoe's lace was caught on a cow's horn. The shoe was now hanging from the cow's horn.

The milkman saw this and threw it into a farmhouse. This was Mary's house! When Mary saw it, she happily thought that the world was indeed round!

18. A Lesson

One day, Rina saw her brother Tim play with a catapult. He climbed up a tree. From there, he saw a bald-headed farmer walking under the tree. "It would be fun to aim at his head," said naughty Tim.

But Rina stopped him, "Tim, no! Don't hurt anyone for fun!"

Tim did not listen to her. He hit the farmer's head with a stone in his catapult. The farmer's head started bleeding. Then, he saw Tim with his catapult. The farmer called out, "You have a very good aim. When the Sheriff comes this way, you should shoot at him too. He will appreciate someone with such a good aim."

Tim was very happy and waited for the Sheriff. As soon as he saw the Sheriff, he hit him too.

The Sheriff got angry and punished Tim for being naughty.

Tim cried out, "Rina, you were right. I am sorry for being so naughty!"

19. The Smart Donkey

A washerman went to the river every day to wash clothes. He sat on the Donkey and rode on it.

The people of the village made fun of him. They said, "Look at that. A fool is riding another fool."

The washerman said, "My Donkey is not a fool. He is smarter than the King's Ministers."

The news of the washerman's comment reached the King very soon. The King called for him and asked, "Why do you think your Donkey is smarter than my Ministers?"

The washerman said, "Your Majesty, one day, while crossing the bridge, my Donkey's feet got caught between the wooden boards. From that day, whenever he reaches that spot, he is very careful. Your Ministers spend a lot of your money, but they have still not repaired the bridge. So, my Donkey is smarter."

The King realised that his Ministers were not doing their jobs.

20. The Jealous Tree

One day, a man was walking on the road. Suddenly, a large stone, lying on the walkway, hit his foot. He pushed the stone under a tree, so that no one else would get hurt.

Then, a painter stopped to rest under the same tree. By accident, some yellow paint from his paintbox fell on the stone.

Next, a flower girl sat under the tree to sort out her flowers. Some flowers fell on the ground near the stone.

When people walked by the tree, they thought the stone was a holy idol. They started worshipping the stone.

The tree became jealous of the stone. "People don't come here for my shade, any more." It kicked the stone away.

When people saw that the stone had moved, they thought the tree was unholy. So, they decided to cut down the tree. The tree was punished for his jealousy.

21. Brave Adam

Once, there lived a brave man named Adam. One day, Adam was walking through a dense and quiet forest.

Suddenly, a group of thieves came out of nowhere. They had guns and knives in their hands. They surrounded Adam and said, "Take out all your money, jewels and valuables. Give them to us."

Adam was not scared. He said, "I will not give you even a penny."

They all started fighting with Adam, who fought with all his might. But, since there were a lot of thieves, they caught him and searched his pockets. They found only a few pennies.

Adam said, "Please don't take that. It is for my poor mother's medicine."

The leader felt bad for him, but praised Adam's courage. He said, "This man has fought for his mother's medicine. He is a brave man. Let him go." He also gave Adam some more money for his mother.

22. Cherry's Baking

Cherry lived in the town. When she saw that Jerome baked yummy pies, cookies and hot cakes, she also wanted to learn baking.

Cherry asked Jerome to teach her. Jerome agreed. In a few days, Cherry became a good baker.

Tina owned a bakery in the town. She teased Cherry, as she did not own a bakery. Cherry got very angry, and challenged Tina to a baking competition. Cherry baked an apple pie and won.

Cherry became very proud now. She teased all the others and thought that she was the best baker in the town.

One day, she challenged Jerome to a baking competition. In her pride, she forgot that Jerome was her teacher!

Cherry baked chocolate chip cookies. Jerome baked a large éclair, filled with tasty cream and strawberry sauce. Thus, Jerome won this time. Everyone now teased Cherry.

She understood that one should never be too proud.

23. Pray with a Pure Heart

Once, a little girl, Sara lived with her parents in a little cottage. Her Father was a thief and her Mother worked all day.

One day, Sara woke up and found her Mother dead.

After that, her Father went to steal every day. When Sara stopped him, he beat her up. Sara prayed to God every day to help her. One day, she woke up in the night. She saw a beautiful Angel.

The Angel said, "Dear Sara, you prayed to God with a pure heart every day. So, He has sent me to help you."

Sara said, "I want my Father to stop stealing, work responsibly and love me." The Angel granted her wish.

The next day, Sara found her Father near her bed. He apologised and went to look for work.

Soon, he started working on a farm. Also, he started loving Sara and always kept her happy.

24. Linda and Tracy

Linda and Tracy lived in an orphanage. The Manager made the girls work all day and gave them little to eat.

Linda and Tracy became very sad and ran away from the orphanage. The next day, they reached a new town.

Then, Linda and Tracy heard two women saying that the Queen was hiring maids for the palace. They went to the palace and were immediately hired. They were very happy and worked hard. They always took care of the Queen. She started depending on them greatly.

After sometime, the Queen's evil Aunt invited her for dinner. Linda and Tracy advised, "One should not trust her. Therefore, you should send one of us and see how the Aunt treats her."

The Queen did as advised and sent Linda. To the Queen's dismay, they found that the Aunt imprisoned Linda.

The Queen sent her guards immediately to get Linda released. She then thanked Linda and Tracy and kept them as her chief advisors!

25. Intelligent Girls

Once, a rich Landlord died. He left behind his three daughters.

According to his will, his two Brothers were to take care of his property and his daughters.

The daughters tried to get in touch with their uncles who lived in foreign lands, but in vain.

Many months passed, when one day, two old Men came to their house and claimed to be their uncles.

The Landlord's daughters were very happy. They gave them all the money and gold and said, "Please keep all these valuables safe with you. We will be ready to go with you tomorrow morning."

At night, the two Men gathered all the valuables and left the house. Suddenly, they found themselves caught by some guards. They were shocked.

The daughters came and said, "We gave you all the valuables to test your intentions. You two are not our father's brothers, but thieves."

Soon, the thieves were sent to prison.

26. The Loyal Servant

Maria lived in a beautiful mansion. Her parents were rich and had many servants.

Maria liked Tess, her governess. Tess had a daughter, Simi. Maria and Simi always played together.

Soon, Maria started going to school but Mini stayed at home, because Tess did not have enough money.

Maria requested her Mother, "Please send Mini to school with me." But she did not bother.

After some days, Maria's Father met with an accident. He was bedridden for months. His business began to suffer and soon they had no money to pay the servants.

Slowly, all the servants left, but Tess was very loyal. She stayed and took care of her master till he was well again.

Now, Maria's Mother was ashamed of her behaviour. She apologised, "I'm sorry Tess. I will start sending Mini to school now."

After that, Maria's Mother brought up Mini like her own daughter.

27. Hannah and the Cruel King

Once, a King married a hundred women. But, he always killed his wives on his wedding night.

When he decided to marry his Minister's daughter, Hannah, the Minister got very worried.

But, Hannah said, "Don't worry, Father. I will not let the King kill me."

The Minister agreed with a heavy heart.

On the wedding night, Hannah said, "Dear King, before you kill me, grant my last wish. I want to tell you an interesting story."

The King agreed and she started the story. The story was extremely interesting and continued till dawn.

Then, Hannah said, "You have spent the entire night listening to the story!"

The King was shocked. He had vowed to kill all his wives on the wedding night. He could not kill Hannah now. He appreciated her intelligence and decided never to kill her. Soon, he fell in love with her and they lived happily ever after.

28. The Greedy Woman

Cindy lived with her cruel Stepmother. The Stepmother made the poor girl work all day and never gave her enough to eat.

One night, Cindy could not sleep due to hunger. She left the house and went to the forest to pick some fruits. Suddenly, she saw some robbers hiding some gold and money behind a rock.

She waited quietly till the robbers left. Then, she took away some coins. She went home and gave them to her Stepmother.

The Stepmother asked her about the place. She was a greedy woman and wanted to take all the coins. So, at night, she went to the forest to steal more. By then, the robbers knew that somebody had stolen their gold.

They were waiting and caught the Stepmother. Cindy pleaded before them to set her free, so they agreed.

The Stepmother was very ashamed. She took good care of Cindy from then.

29. Uneducated Rose

Once, a rich Man lived in a big house. He was married to an uneducated girl, Rose. She was beautiful but the Man did not love her. He was not happy marrying an illiterate.

One night, the Man came extremely exhausted in his room. Suddenly, he had a heart attack. Rose, at once, gave him first aid. Then, she called the doctor.

The doctor told the Man, "You are lucky to have an intelligent wife."

The Man was ashamed of his behaviour.

Rose took great care of him during his illness. His friends came to visit him and greatly appreciated his wife's hospitality and good manners.

One day, he asked her, "How can you do all this, without being educated?"

She smiled and replied, "My poor parents could not educate me, but that does not make me dumb!"

The Man agreed and never disrespected her again.

30. Katie and Beauty

Once, a girl named Katie lived with her parents on a big farm. Her Father gave Katie a beautiful pony, Beauty, on her birthday. She was extremely happy and wanted to ride immediately.

Her Father warned her, "Beauty is a naughty pony. Also, you are not a good rider yet. So, you should not go alone to ride him."

Then, he promised to take her for a ride the next day. Katie was disheartened. But, she did not say anything.

When everybody slept at night, she quietly went to the stable. Then, she took Beauty out and tried to ride him.

Beauty was not friendly with her and kicked her hard as she went to sit on it. Katie fell on the ground and cried loudly.

She had broken her leg and could not ride Beauty for the next three months. Katie was ashamed that she had not listened to her Father.

1. Act of Kindness

Bertha and Penelope were sisters. Their parents were poor.

One evening, Bertha and Penelope saw a Man. He was wearing a thin robe and was shivering in the cold.

Penelope took off her sweater and covered the Man with it. This made Bertha very angry. She said, "Penelope! Why did you give him your sweater? Now mum and dad will have to buy a new one for you!"

Penelope smiled and said, "No, I will manage with my old sweater. This man needed the sweater more than I did."

That night, Penelope went to her room after dinner. She prayed before going to bed. When she opened her eyes after praying, she saw a large chest beside her. She opened it and found lots of woollen clothes inside, enough for her whole family!

There was also a note there, which said, 'Thank you for saving your Angel from the cold.'

2. The Dancing Shoes

Once, there lived a little girl named Karen. She lived in the country, and her family was very rich.

Karen's Mother fed Karen with tasty food and dressed her in pretty clothes and lovely shoes. Karen was a healthy girl. Her face glowed and she was beautiful. However, she was also quite proud of her looks.

One day, as Karen was walking in the forest, she saw a pair of shiny new shoes lying behind a bush. She thought, "Oh! What pretty shoes! They must be made for a lovely girl like me!" Thus, she put on the shoes.

However, the moment Karen put on the new shoes, her feet began tapping. Soon, she was dancing, and could not stop! She danced from the forest to the village, and then to the town, but no one could help her.

Night fell and Karen was still dancing. By now she was back in the forest. She was very tired. Suddenly, she saw a sparkling silver Angel in front of her. The Angel was holding a sword. He said, "You have been punished because you are very vain, Karen!" and vanished.

Crying bitterly, Karen found a woodcutter's axe and cut her feet with the axe. She wept, "I lost my feet because of vanity!"

That day onwards, Karen began living in the forest. She was kind to the animals and lived on berries and other fruits of the jungle. One day, the Angel appeared before her again. This time, he was holding a wreath of roses instead of the sword.

The Angel said, "You have mended your ways, dear Karen! You shall not suffer any more!" And he gave her the wreath of roses. The moment Karen held it in her hands, colourful petals flew around her. There was a flash of golden light, and Karen got her feet back. She rushed home happily.

3. April's Love

April was a beautiful woman. She lived in the mountains with her husband, Ethan. The couple loved each other dearly.

One day, Ethan returned home after collecting wood for the fireplace. As he was setting up the logs in the fireplace, he saw a present hidden behind it. It was wrapped in blue ribbon. On top of it, there was a card that said, 'I love you.'

Ethan thought that April had bought the present for another man and that she loved someone else now. He was very angry and did not talk to April for three days.

On the fourth day, Ethan woke up and found a present wrapped in blue ribbon near his pillow. It was the one that April had hidden! Then, April came with a breakfast tray and said, "Happy birthday, Ethan! I love you!"

Ethan felt ashamed for doubting his wife and apologised to her.

4. Emma's Doubt

Emma was a beautiful young woman. When she was little, her Mother always taught her to be kind and polite to others. "Always help those in need, Emma," she would tell her.

Emma grew up and became a governess. However, none of her friends worked. They spent their time dressing up, curling their hair and thinking of their weddings.

Soon, Emma began doubting her work. She thought, 'My friends enjoy free time and here I am, working away day and night.' Soon, she stopped working as a governess. She also started dressing up like her friends.

However, some days later, she began feeling useless. She missed her work of helping people. She realised that by working, her life was better than that of her friends. She went to her Mother and said, "Forgive me for doubting your lesson, Mother. I will become a governess again and happily help people now."

5. Fight of the Goddesses

Thousands of years ago, there was a city in the sky. It was called Flyville. Goddesses, fairies and angels lived there. Athena was the Queen of Flyville. Her magic was the most powerful.

Iris was the Goddess of Knowledge at Flyville and Vienna was the Goddess of Beauty. One day, Iris and Vienna had a fight. Each thought herself to be better.

"I am the most knowledgeable of all!" said Iris.

"I am the most beautiful woman ever!" snapped Vienna.

Soon, Athena came to know about Iris and Vienna's argument. She was very angry because they were disturbing the peace of Flyville.

Athena went to them and said, "Neither of you is perfect. Beauty and knowledge should be together to become valuable. Now stop fighting or I will give your powers to one woman who will be beautiful and wise."

Iris and Vienna realised their mistake and stopped fighting.

6. Janine's Magic

Once, there was a woman called Janine. She had no job, so she went to the nearby town and told everyone that she could do magic.

One day, some thieves struck in the town and robbed many houses in one night. The people went to Janine for help.

Though she could not perform any magic, Janine could not admit the truth. She had to agree to help them. She asked every town member to come to her one by one, so that she could identify the thief.

When the first Man came, Janine said, "Oh, you are the first man," meaning that he was the first person who had come to see her. But, the villager was actually the first thief! He was shocked and terrified. He fell at Janine's feet and revealed the names of the other thieves.

The happy people rewarded Janine with gold coins.

7. Sarah's Conscience

Once, a poor girl named Sarah wanted to become rich. She met a group of girls. They said, "We promise to make you rich if you work with us."

Sarah asked, "What would be the work like?"

They said, "We steal precious items from various shops."

Sarah was shocked and said, "I don't want to steal."

The gang laughed at her and said, "Then you can never become rich."

Sarah hesitated but accepted their offer.

The next day, they went in a gift shop and stole things. But, Sarah could not steal.

Suddenly, the Sheriff came and caught all of them including Sarah. They were thoroughly searched and stolen items were recovered from them.

When the Sheriff searched Sarah, he could not find anything and let her go. Her inner-self had not allowed her to steal and saved her from being punished.

Sarah felt relieved for not having agreed to follow the line of crime.

8. Captain

Marlene was the captain of her softball team. She had won many games and the other girls respected her a lot.

But, soon Marlene became proud. She felt she did not need any practise.

The team's Coach said, "If you don't practise seriously, your performance will suffer."

But, Marlene did not bother. She also started bullying other team-mates, specially a new girl, Olivia.

Olivia was also a good player and soon became the star of the team. Marlene felt very jealous, but did not change her attitude.

She became extremely careless and her performance became very bad. Soon, the Coach decided to make Olivia the captain.

Marlene could not believe this and went running to him. The Coach said, "You stopped respecting your game and ignored my warnings. You should never take anything lightly, even if you are at the top – in fact, more so if you are the top!"

Now, Marlene understood and played sincerely.

9. Stormy Night

Once, a group of Girls decided to go to the beach. They relaxed on the beach during the day.

At night, the First Girl suggested to go fishing. Since the sea looked calm, the others also agreed.

They hired a boat and went into the sea. The Girls could not catch any fish. So, the First Girl suggested going deeper into the sea.

The others hesitated but then agreed. They enjoyed each other's company and did not realise that they had come very far from the land.

All of a sudden, it began raining and the waves became higher. Soon, their small boat started filling with water. They panicked and prayed to God for the rain to stop.

Fortunately, they saw some fishermen in a huge boat. They saw the Girls and took them in their boat to the shore.

Once they reached safely, the Girls decided never to take such risks again.

10. Friendship between Equals

Jane and Georgia were very good friends. They spent the entire day at school together.

One day, a new student, Elmer joined their school. He and Jane soon became friends.

Elmer was very rich. He told Jane about his games and toys all day.

One day, Jane asked, "Elmer, can I come home to see your toys?"

Elmer agreed but Georgia did not want Jane to go. Jane did not listen and went with Elmer.

Elmer took Jane to his room and showed her the toys. Jane really liked the toys but broke one of them by mistake.

Immediately, Elmer shouted, "You stupid girl! You have ruined my toy. Get out of my house."

Jane was hurt and ran home. Georgia wiped her tears and comforted her. Then, she said, "We should not make friends with people who are very different from us."

Now, Jane understood her mistake.

11. Stupid Janet

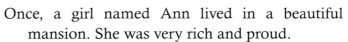

Once, a girl named Ann lived in a beautiful mansion. She was very rich and proud.

One day, her best friend, Janet came to visit her. She said, "I am getting married to Mr. Philips soon."

Ann was disappointed and said, "Dear Janet, you are my best friend. You should not get married to an ordinary man like Mr. Philips. I will find you a better match."

Janet broke her engagement and Ann advised her to pursue Mr. Rogers who was a wealthy man.

Janet did as told but Mr. Rogers found Janet too ordinary. Thus, he rejected her proposal.

Janet was heart-broken. She went to Ann for sympathy. But now, Ann had no time for her.

Poor Janet was completely alone. She did not use her own mind and acted on her proud friend's will. Therefore, she suffered and could not get married for a long time.

12. Aunt's Justice

Once, four sisters lived together in a house. Emma, the eldest, almost ruled over the younger sisters after their parents' death. The younger sisters carried Emma's orders, as they were afraid of her severe punishments.

One day, Emma's Aunt came to stay with them. She was very angry at Emma's unjust behaviour.

She called all the sisters including Emma and said, "Since I am the eldest, you have to follow my instructions."

Then, she gave Emma a list of duties and scolded her the minute she failed. Emma felt very bad and cried all day. Her younger sisters consoled her.

Now, Emma felt ashamed of treating her younger sisters badly. She apologised to them. Aunt saw Emma repent and said, "You cannot justify bad treatment saying that you are older. You should not scold your sisters unnecessarily."

Emma understood her mistake and apologised to her Aunt as well.

13. Alice

Once, a poor girl, Alice lived with her Mother. Her Mother worked extremely hard to send her to a good school.

However, Alice always felt ashamed of being poor. She always demanded money for new things.

One day, Alice's Mother fell ill and wanted to visit the doctor, but Alice insisted that she wanted money for the school picnic.

Mother explained, "If I give you this money, I will not have anything left to buy the medicines."

Alice did not bother about her Mother's health and forced her to give the money.

When Alice came back from the picnic, she found her Mother lying unconscious on the floor. She rushed her to the Doctor's house. Her Mother stayed in bed for several days before she was well again.

Alice hated herself for being selfish. She promised her Mother that she would study well and also help in her work during her free time.

14. Myra's Horse

Myra lived with her parents on a huge farm. The farm had many horses. Myra's favourite horse was a black pony, Austin. She loved him dearly and took great care of him.

One day, Myra's Father said, "I have bought a new business in the city. So we will have to sell our farm and shift soon."

Myra was heartbroken. She asked, "Father, can we not take Austin?"

He replied, "We will not have space to keep him there."

Myra hugged Austin and cried for hours before they left the farm. The Man who bought the farm was very kind. He said, "You can come and visit Austin whenever you feel like."

Myra felt better and left. Every few months, she visited the farm and spent time with Austin. Soon the Farm Owner's Son fell in love with Myra and married her.

Austin was extremely happy to have her back on the farm again.

15. Manor Farm

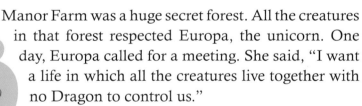

Manor Farm was a huge secret forest. All the creatures in that forest respected Europa, the unicorn. One day, Europa called for a meeting. She said, "I want a life in which all the creatures live together with no Dragon to control us."

The creatures were thrilled and welcomed Europa's idea.

However, three nights later, Europa died. All creatures were very sad and depressed now. But, three young Centaurs decided to work on Europa's dream and make it come true.

The other creatures hesitated, as they did not trust the youngsters as much as the old wise Europa. But, the Centaurs convinced them. They made a plan and explained it to all the creatures.

So, one night, the creatures attacked the Dragon and chased him away from the secret forest. All agreed that if it were not for the young Centaurs, they would never have been free.

16. Kind Tia

Long ago, a pony, Tia was adopted by Mrs. Havisham. Tia tried her best to guard the home of her mistress, all day.

Mrs. Havisham loved her and took great care of her. She fed her cotton candy and gave her soft blankets to sleep on.

Some Street Dogs lived in the neighbourhood. They were very jealous of Tia. They barked and insulted Tia, but she did not pay any attention to their insults.

One day, Tia saw that some young boys were throwing stones at the Street Dogs. They were badly hurt. Tia could not hold herself back. She ran out of the gate towards the boys, as if to hit them.

The boys got scared and ran away.

The Street Dogs were ashamed of their bad behaviour in the past. They apologised to Tia. She forgave them and from that day, Tia and the Street Dogs became friends.

17. The Rock Fairy

A very long time ago, there was a beautiful village surrounded by green mountains and colourful flowers. At one end of the village, was a rock statue that looked like a sleeping Fairy.

One year, there was no rain and the village pond went dry.

The villagers were worried and said, "Our crops will fail and the cattle will die, if it doesn't rain soon."

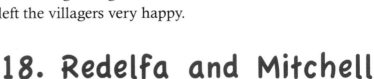

The village children overheard the adults and decided to please the Fairy by taking bouquets of flowers to her.

The next day, all the children gathered by the statue with flowers and prayed to the Fairy.

After a few hours, a dry wind carried some flower petals to the Fairy's nose. The Fairy twitched her nose and opened her eyes. She sneezed so loudly that the dry ground opened and a fountain of water came gushing out!

The Fairy vanished, but left the villagers very happy.

18. Redelfa and Mitchell

Redelfa was a German princess, the elder child of her parents, and was extremely spoilt. She liked to waste her time carelessly.

Redelfa's mother, the Queen, was old and worried about her daughter's careless behaviour. She called Redelfa to her chamber and said, "Dear daughter! Since we do not have a son, you will be the next Queen. It is time you learn to perform your duties sincerely."

Redelfa listened to her mother absent-mindedly, and continued to waste time and money.

The Queen had another daughter named Mitchell. However, the Royal Priest told the Queen that Mitchell was the younger sister and could not succeed to the throne.

Soon, the time came to declare the next Queen. The old Queen surprised everyone by declaring Mitchell as the next Queen. Mitchell was a responsible and humble girl. Everyone was overjoyed at the news.

Redelfa was ashamed in the crowded court. She had learnt her lesson, but it was too late now!

19. Mona's Cousin

A little girl called Mona lived with her parents in a cottage near the forest.

One sad day, Mona's Uncle passed away and her Aunt, and cousin, Adam, came to live with them. Mona's parents started taking care of Adam also. Mona felt jealous and did not talk to Adam at all.

One day, Mona had a fight with Adam and ran into the nearby forest. She sat under a tree and cried. Just then, she saw Adam running towards her with a stick. But, he went towards the branch of the tree just above her and hit a snake, which was just about to jump on Mona.

Mona pulled Adam back and said, "Leave it, and let's go home."

Mona understood that Adam was like her brother and that her parents loved both of them. That day on, Mona and Adam became best friends and lived happily ever after.

20. A Dog Called Cookie

Ramona had a wonderful dog. She called him 'Cookie' for he loved butterscotch cookies!

Cookie loved to play in the garden all day and chase squirrels into Ramona's neighbour, Mrs. Tweddle's garden.

Mrs. Tweddle was old and lived alone. She did not like Cookie spoiling her pretty flowerbeds and soft, green grass. Thus, she always shouted at Cookie. Sometimes, she even hit him with a stick.

One afternoon, Cookie was in the garden. Just then, he heard a shout from Mrs. Tweedle's house. Cookie ran to Mrs. Tweedle's house. There he saw Mrs. Tweedle lying on the floor. She had slipped and fainted.

Cookie ran back home and barked loudly. Ramona's mother, at once, ran after Cookie. She found Mrs. Tweddle and took her to the hospital.

Soon, Mrs. Tweddle was better and returned home. From that day, she loved Cookie and gave him his favourite butterscotch cookies to eat.

21. Pearl's Doll

Pearl's Aunt Stella came to visit her from Africa. She stayed for two weeks and while leaving, gifted Pearl an African doll.

One day, Pearl took her doll to the park to show it to her friends. As they were playing, Pearl's friend, Wilma, broke the doll by mistake. Pearl ran home, crying.

Pearl never spoke to Wilma again. Wilma was very sad that she had broken Pearl's doll. She wanted to get a new doll for Pearl, but her family was very poor. So, Wilma worked in the local inn after school for a week. She wiped tables and helped in the kitchen.

Then, she finally bought a new doll for Pearl and gifted it to her.

When Pearl came to know how Wilma had got the money, she started crying. She hugged Wilma and said, "Wilma, you are a true friend. Come, let us play together."

22. Serena and Leona

Once, Serena took her sister, Leona's chocolate from her bag and ate it. Leona was very angry and decided to take revenge.

The next day, when Serena came home from school, her Mother shouted, "How many times have I told you not to leave your room in a mess?"

Serena ran upstairs and was horrified to see the condition of the room. She tidied the mess and knew that Leona had done it.

Once, after school, Serena and her friends fought with Leona. Leona cried all the way home and told her Mother what had happened.

When Serena came home, Mother said, "Girls, you are blessed to have each other to depend on. Love and forgive each other for you will be with each other all your life. If you won't take care of each other, you will both suffer."

The girls promised their Mother that they would never fight.

23. Honest Trisha

Once, there lived a girl called Trisha. One day, Trisha's cousin Kate came to live with them.

Kate was very naughty. Whenever Trisha's parents went out, Kate would mess up the kitchen and the sitting room and throw Trisha's father's important papers out of the window.

Every time something went wrong, Trisha's parents blamed her. She would try to explain, but they would not listen at all. Her parents decided to send Trisha to a boarding school. She was terribly hurt.

Just before she was to leave for the school, Trisha spoke to her mother, "I know you never believed me when I said I did no wrong. I still say the same. It was not I but Kate."

Now, while Trisha was in school, Kate again did all the naughty things. Trisha's parents realised their mistake. They, at once, sent Kate back to her parents and got Trisha back home.

24. Teresa's Lobo

Nelly and her family had just moved into a lovely house, overlooking the sea.

In a cupboard in the bedroom, Nelly found a teddy bear. She didn't know why, but she decided to call him Lobo.

That night, Nelly saw a dream. In her dream, a little girl, lying on a bed, said to her, "Nelly, please give me Lobo. He is mine."

The next morning, Nelly told her Mother about the dream. Then, they went to their neighbour and asked about a small girl. He said, "Oh! A girl called Teresa used to live here. She now lives in a small house in the town."

Nelly and her Mother took Lobo to meet Teresa. Nelly was shocked to see the girl of her dream, lying on a bed.

Teresa's love for Lobo had made it possible for her to come in Nelly dreams. Nelly happily gave Lobo to Teresa.

25. The Night Fairy

Lina was a little girl who lived with her parents.

One day, Lina's Mother fell very ill and died. Lina was very sad and she cried day and night for her Mother. She missed her terribly.

Then, one evening, Lina went and sat on a rock near their house. That was her Mother's favourite place. But, when Lina was coming back, it had become dark. She fell and hurt her knee and cried out, "Oh Mother! I wish you were here!"

Suddenly, Lina saw a shadow walk towards her. The shadow said, "Lina, I am the Night Fairy."

Then, she picked up Lina gently in her arms and carried her home.

Soon, Lina was on her bed and fast asleep. From then on, whenever Lina was in trouble, the Night Fairy came to help her. Lina never missed her Mother again as she knew that the Night Fairy was her Mother!

26. The Best Birthday Present

Fiona was a very spoilt girl. She always wanted expensive gifts and would cry if she did not get them.

It was Fiona's birthday one day. Fiona and her Father went to a bakery to order a cake. Fiona saw a little girl there with a bandaged hand. Fiona started talking to her. The girl said, "I love to study but I have to help my Father. Yesterday, I was carrying a heavy tray. I fell and broke my arm."

Fiona was very touched at the little girl's words.

The next day, everybody was preparing for Fiona's birthday. But, Fiona was unhappy. She said, "Father, I don't want to have a party or expensive toys. Please send the girl in the bakery to school. That will be the best birthday gift for me!"

Fiona's Father agreed at once. He thanked God, for the meeting with the poor girl had changed his spoilt daughter for the better.

27. Caring Sarah

Once, there lived a little girl called Sarah, with her Mother. Sarah's Mother worked as a maid in the Queen's palace.

One day, Sarah's Mother dropped a pretty vase in the Queen's chambers. The Queen was very angry and shouted at her. Poor Sarah's Mother finished her work and went home, crying.

When she reached home, she saw Sarah playing outside. She shouted, "You play all day! Why could you have not made some tea for me? I work so hard for you, what do you do for me?"

Then, she went inside the house and saw that hot, steaming food was kept on the small dining table.

Sarah said, "Mother, I knew you would be tired, so I cooked dinner for you."

Sarah's Mother was very ashamed. She hugged Sarah and said, "Sarah, I'm sorry. You are so caring. I will never take out my anger on you ever!"

28. The Joy of Music

Susannah was a very beautiful and talented young woman. However, she was all alone in the world and felt very sad. She taught singing at the local school.

One day, Emma, a little girl in Susannah's class was crying. Susannah found out that Emma's mother had died a week ago. Susannah said, "Emma, don't cry. If your Mother looks down on you from Heaven, she will be sad to see you cry. Come, let us sing."

Emma started singing with Susannah. Soon, her sadness disappeared.

After a few months, Emma said to Susannah, "My Father wants to meet you. He was very sad and I made him sing with me. Now, he feels better, too. He wants to thank you."

Thus, Susannah met Emma's Father. They both liked each other so much, that soon, they were married. So, now Susannah has a family and Emma has a mother!

29. A Mother's Heart

One day, the Fairy Queen was flying over a village with the other Fairies. Just then, they saw a Woman who was hugging and kissing a dark and scrawny baby. She was also singing songs to him.

The Queen Fairy wondered, "How can this Woman love a dark and scrawny baby?"

A wise Fairy replied, "Looks don't matter to a mother! To her, her own child is the most beautiful in the world!"

The Queen said, "Let us see. Bring me the most beautiful baby in the world!"

The next day, the wise Fairy said, "We have arranged a competition to choose the most beautiful baby."

At the competition, all the Fairies, Elves, and animals came. Each mother said that her baby was the most beautiful!

The Fairy Queen blessed them all and said, "Now I understand a mother's heart. She loves her child blindly, no matter how he looks!"

30. Bella's Home

Bella lived in a cottage in the mountains. The mountains were covered with grass and trees and looked very green.

In the spring, flowers would bloom all over. Then, the green mountains would be speckled with pink, blue, purple, orange, yellow and red. Bella looked at the mountains and enjoyed their beauty.

Bella would sit under the shady trees and read her books. When she felt hungry, she picked juicy berries from the trees and ate them.

Sometimes, it rained in the mountains. The mountains look greener then. Bella would put her arm out of her cottage's window and enjoy the raindrops on her palm. When the sun shone after the rains, a large and beautiful rainbow would appear in the sky. It had seven colours that glowed in the sun.

Bella loved her home and was glad that she did not live in the city, like her friends.

31. Daffodils

Zenith was a poor little girl. Every day, she would wake up early in the morning and work in Mrs. Gilbert's garden.

Mrs. Gilbert was a kind woman. She gave Zenith lunch and some coins at the end of the day. Then, Zenith would use those coins to buy dinner and breakfast for the next day. One day, Zenith was watering the tulips. When she started watering the daffodils, she was amazed to see them growing before her very eyes! The daffodils grew and grew until they became as tall as Zenith.

Then, the daffodils opened their petals. Soon, little creatures started coming out of the petals. They were Angels with wings!

The little Angels said, "A little girl like you should read and play, not work like adults. Come with us."

Thus, they wrapped Zenith in their wings and flew her to the clouds where they took care of her.

1. Salty Doughnuts

Monica was a sweet little girl. She loved doughnuts.

Every day, Monica would help her Mother in some household chores. She would take the clothes off the clothesline, lay the table and clean her room. Then, Mother would buy a doughnut for her.

Monica's favourite place was Mr. Jones' doughnut shop. He made the tastiest doughnuts. His doughnuts came in chocolate, apple, cinnamon and caramel flavours. They were topped with strawberry jam, chocolate sauce and nuts. Monica loved them all!

However, one day, when Monica tucked into a chocolate doughnut, she found it salty! She went to Mr. Jones to get it replaced. But, at the kitchen's doorway, Monica saw his naughty son, Tim, emptying a jar of salt in the dough mix. Now she understood why the doughnut tasted salty!

Monica ran and told Mr. Jones about Tim. Mr. Jones scolded Tim and thanked Monica. He then gave her a box of yummy doughnuts, free!

2. Grandmother

Zena's Grandmother was a very old lady. Her hair was white. When sunshine fell on her hair, it looked silver. She also had wrinkles on her face and hands. However, her eyes were very kind and bright. Zena felt very happy, whenever her Grandmother looked at her with her beautiful eyes.

Zena always went to her Grandmother's room every night, for a bedtime story. One night, she asked, "Grandma, why do you keep this old, dried rose with you all the time?"

Grandmother said, "This rose is many years old. When I was a young woman, I used to visit the town garden every day to collect flowers. One such day, a handsome man sat next to me on the bench. It was your Grandfather! We fell in love, and he gave me this rose. It was fresh and beautiful then. Now he is no more, but this old rose reminds me of that day. That is why I keep it with me."

Thus, Grandmother completed her story and Zena went to bed. The next day, Zena's parents told her that her Grandmother had gone to heaven, while she was sleeping. Zena felt very sad, for she knew her dear Grandmother was now dead.

Grandmother looked beautiful in her black coffin, and her lips looked as if she were smiling. Zena kissed her Grandmother's forehead and placed the dried rose next to her. Zena felt that she would want to take the memory of Grandfather with her to heaven too.

A few days later, Zena visited the graveyard to lay flowers on her Grandmother's grave. There she saw, that beautiful and sweet-smelling roses had blossomed around her grave. Zena felt very happy. She said, "Grandma is happy and peaceful now. These roses tell me so! My dear Grandma is with Grandpa!"

3. Candles and Light

Mrs. Lockhart was an old lady. She lived alone in a cottage. She made candles for the Women of the village. They all loved her.

Mrs. Lockhart made candles of all shapes and sizes. She put some perfume in them so that they smelled like flowers. Then, she would paint them in bright colours.

However, lately, Mrs. Lockhart's candles were not so good. Sometimes they were not scented, sometimes they were not coloured.

The Women visited Mrs. Lockhart and asked her why she did not make pretty candles any more.

"I am so old that I cannot work properly any more," sobbed poor Mrs. Lockhart.

The Women felt very sad. They said, "You should not live alone and work at this age. Stay at each of our houses, in turn. We will take care of you!"

Thus, Mrs. Lockhart never had to work again and spent the rest of her days, happily.

4. Anna's Lesson

Anna was a little girl, who loved to dance. Her Mother noticed her interest and decided to make her join the Ballet School.

Anna was very excited about learning ballet. She put together her ballet dress and shoes and went to the Ballet School with her Mother.

However, when the class began, Anna saw that the teacher, Mr. Harrison, was very strict. He would scold the students if they did not dance properly. Anna felt so scared that she could not dance correctly at all. Mr. Harrison scolded her, too.

Anna ran home in tears and told her Mother about Mr. Harrison. Mother hugged her and said, "Anna, you should not worry about the teacher. Just concentrate on the lesson. Remember that you love to dance!"

Anna understood her Mother's words. She wiped her tears and said, "You are right, Mother. I will do my best to learn ballet."

5. Fair Josie

Josie was a pretty, fair little girl, but was also vain. 'I am the most beautiful. So, I deserve the prettiest things!' she would think. She would not let her friends touch her toys.

Soon, Josie's friends became fed up of her. They stopped visiting her. Now, Josie was very sad. She did not understand why her friends would not talk to her any more.

Weeping, Josie ran to the backyard and sat among the grape vines. Suddenly, one of the grapes started glowing purple. The light became brighter and turned into a beautiful woman dressed in purple clothes.

It was the Purple Fairy! She said, "Josie, what will you do with your toys when you don't have friends to share them with? Do not be vain, and share your things. You will be happier!" and she turned back into a grape.

Josie learnt her lesson and apologised to her friends.

6. House of Gold

Sarah was a very rich woman. Yet, she was never content. She always wanted more things. She thought, 'I can buy anything!'

One day, Sarah decided to buy a house of gold. She went to many people and asked, "Please tell me the way to a shop that sells gold houses." But, no one could help her.

After some time, Sarah saw an Old Man and asked the same question. He asked, "Do you help the needy? Do you teach poor children? Do you read to the old?"

Confused, Sarah replied, "No, I don't do any of those things."

The Old Man said, "You will have a house of gold, if you do them."

Thus, Sarah started helping the poor and the old. These good deeds made her very happy. She knew what the Old Man meant. By doing the good deeds, her heart had become a house of gold!

7. The Haunted House

Pansy was a sweet little girl. She obeyed her parents and studied hard. However, she was superstitious. She thought that the black cats were unlucky. She even believed in evil spirits.

One night, when Pansy was sleeping in her room, she heard some sounds from the ceiling. She sprang up. It seemed as if someone were stomping on the roof! She thought it might be a cat – what if it was a black one! Or, maybe it was an evil spirit or a ghost – Pansy ran to her parents' room, screaming, "Help! Ghost!"

Pansy's parents came running to her room. When they also heard the sounds from the ceiling, her father went up the stairs to find out the cause.

He returned after some time, laughing. He said, "Pansy, your room is right under the attic. I went there and found a family of mice jumping around. That was causing the noise. There are no such things as ghosts!"

Pansy felt better now. She also realised that one should not be superstitious.

8. Judie's Wish

Judie was a young woman who lived in the country. She painted very well and wanted to become a painter.

However, Judie's parents did not like painting. "You should work at the farm, like the other women," they would say. Soon, Judie started working at the farm. But, she felt sad, for she no longer had the time to paint.

One day, Judie's Mother went to fetch her from the farm. She saw Judie working hard, but she looked very sad. Mother said, "Judie, you are tired. Don't work now."

At once, Judie started painting. When Mum went to her room, she saw Judie smiling and painting a landscape.

At dinner, Mother said, "Judie, I noticed you today. Painting is the only work that makes you happy. You should be a painter. We are sorry for holding you back."

Judie was very happy now. She hugged her Mother tight!

9. Grandma's Necklace

Emily's Grandma always wore a beautiful pearl necklace. She never took it off.

One day, Emily was alone with her Grandma. Suddenly, a Thief broke into the house. He shouted, "Give me all the money in the house. Otherwise, I shall kill you!"

Grandma said, "Spare us! Here, take my valuable necklace instead."

Then, she took off her beautiful pearl necklace and gave it to the Thief, who ran away.

Emily was stunned. She said, "Grandma, why did you give your precious necklace away?"

Grandma said, "Your life is more important, dear. Besides, my necklace will return to me."

Suddenly, Emily saw bright little spots of light coming through the window. As the light spots came closer, she saw that they were small, glowing fairies! The Fairies now joined their hands and turned into the pearl necklace.

Grandma said, "Emily, this necklace is yours now. It will protect you."

10. Baby Sister

There were two girls, named Alice and Aldis. They were best friends.

One day, Aldis went to Alice's house to play. Alice said, "Aldis, I have a new baby sister. Come and see."

Alice took Aldis to a room that was decorated in pink. There was a beautiful white crib in the middle of the room. Aldis peeked into the crib and saw a little baby. The baby was very cute.

Alice said, "Isn't my sister pretty? I can't wait to play with her."

Aldis said, "Yes Alice, She is very sweet. I wish I had a sister like that."

Aldis ran home to her Mother and said, "Mother, I want a baby sister just like Alice's. She looks so sweet, just like a doll!"

Mom smiled, "Sure, Alice! We will also have a baby in our house, after we celebrate your next birthday."

Aldis was very happy. She said, "Thank you very much, Mother."

11. The Snowman

It was a cold, wintry day. Emma and Alexandra were playing in the house.

After some time they were bored. Emma said, "Let's go outside and make a snowman!"

So, they went and asked their Mother. She said, "That is a good idea. A snowman will look very good on our driveway."

So the girls wore their jackets, gloves, caps and snow boots. They went out and started making their snowman. Mother came out with olives, a carrot, buttons, scarf and a hat.

The girls used the olives for the eyes and the carrot for the nose. They used some sticks to make the mouth and arms.

Then, Mother helped put the hat on his head. She also tied the scarf around his neck. It was really fun!

Everyone who saw the snowman loved it. They said it was the best snowman they had ever seen.

12. Messy Mary

Nelly and Mary were sisters. Nelly took care of all her things. She always kept everything in its place.

But, Mary was different. She never kept anything in its place. So, she was always searching for things and asking her Mother or Nelly to help her find them.

One day, Mother said, "Mary, why don't you learn to put away your things in their place? It would make it a lot easier for all of us."

But Mary did not listen. One day, while going to school, Mary could not find her homework notebook. She ran all over the house looking for it, and what did she see! Her pet dog, Bruno, had chewed up her notebook! All her hardwork had gone to waste and she would be punished. Now Mary realised the importance of keeping things in their place.

13. Angelina Goes to School

It was the first day of school for Angelina. She was very excited. Her Mother dropped her at school.

As she entered the class, the Teacher said, "Welcome to school, Angelina. Is this your first day here?"

"Yes it is," said Angelina shyly.

Now that her Mother had left, she was feeling a little scared. She looked around the classroom. Some children were playing with toys. Others were reading books.

But, the Teacher was very nice. She read a funny book about a little girl who tried to bake a large cake by herself.

Then they went to the playground and played with a ball for some time. Angelina even played on the swing.

When they came back, the Teacher gave them cookies and milk. Then, Mother came to pick up Angelina. She asked, "Did you like school, Angelina?"

Angelina replied, "I love school. Can I come every day?"

14. Generous Anna

Anna felt like having an ice cream. She went and looked for her moneybox. But it had no money. "Oh! No! It's empty," she said.

So, she went to her Mother and asked, "Mother, can I have some money to buy an ice cream? The ice cream man is in our street."

"What happened to the money in your moneybox?" asked her Mother.

"I bought some flowers with that money yesterday. Look, it is empty," and she showed Mother her empty box.

"I will give you some money. Come with me," said Mother.

Anna's Mother gave her the money. When Anna went to buy the ice cream, her Friend was crying, "My Mother has gone to Grandma's and will return next week. I miss her!"

So, Anna bought the ice cream and gave it to her Friend. She stopped crying and enjoyed the ice cream. Anna was glad that her Friend was happy again.

15. Daren, the Dreamer

Daren was a young man. He always lived in his dream world. He did not work at all and lived on the money left by his dead father.

His friends suggested, "Daren, you must start working."

But, Daren did not want to do any small jobs. He kept dreaming all day of becoming a rich landlord. He loved a girl, Helena.

One day, Helena came to him and said, "Daren, my father is marrying me to a rich man."

Daren was very upset. He said, "I told your father that I will definitely become a big man, one day."

Helena replied, "My father says that lazy people like you keep dreaming, but do not make any effort to turn their dreams into reality. So, you can never be rich."

Daren realised his mistake, but could not do anything now. It was too late and his ladylove, Helena, was married to another man.

16. An Overconfident Knight

Once, an overconfident knight, Pedro lived in a kingdom. One day, he went to the court and said, "Dear Queen, I can beat anybody in a sword fight."

The Queen was amused and said, "It is not a good quality to be overconfident."

Pedro got annoyed and said, "I challenge any knight to fight and defeat me."

Now, the Queen decided to teach him a lesson. She organised a duel the next day.

Many people gathered in the arena to watch the duel. Soon, the fight began between Pedro and the Queen's Knight. In no time, Pedro was beaten. He was ashamed and left the kingdom.

Next day, the courtiers asked the Queen, "We want to meet the one who defeated proud Pedro."

The bold Queen smiled and said, "It was me, your Queen. I wanted to teach him a lesson."

17. The Foolish Mistress

Once, a rich Landlady wanted to hire a servant. A poor peasant, Sancho decided to work for her. His Wife tried to stop him and said, "The Landlady is extremely foolish. Nobody wants to work for her."

Sancho replied, "I don't care till the time she pays me well."
After this, Sancho started working for the Landlady.

The Landlady could be fooled very easily. Every day, people fooled her for their benefit and took lots of money from her.

At times, people came just for amusement and played various pranks and tricks on the Landlady.

One day, a couple came and said, "Dear Landlady, if you whip your servant, Sancho a hundred times, all your health problems will disappear forever."

The foolish Landlady got Sancho mercilessly whipped. The cruel couple got the desired entertainment and left, but Sancho cried in pain all night. The next day, he repented not listening to his Wife.

18. Sensible Carol

Two friends, Jim and Carol studied science in a university. Jim was very ambitious. He wanted to make a great discovery.

One day, he told Carol, "I want to do an experiment to make dead humans come alive."

Carol said, "One's life and death is God's decision. You should not interfere with the rules of God." Jim did not understand.

At night, Jim started his experiment. After a few days, he was successful, but was shocked to see that he had created a monster instead of a human being.

Jim ran out of the room for Carol's help. She was a good friend and agreed to help him.

Carol was courageous and entered the monster's room with a big axe. She hit the monster with the axe and killed it.

Jim was saved and thanked his friend. He also apologised for not listening to her and interfering with God's decisions.

19. Lily's Forest Trip

Once, a little girl, Lily lived with her parents near the forest. Her Father was a woodcutter.

One day, he was going to cut wood in the forest. He saw Lily follow him and said, "You cannot come with me. There are many wild animals in the forest."

Lily wanted to see the forest. She pretended to go back but went deep into the forest instead.

Soon, she got tired and wanted to return home. But, she had lost her way. She cried aloud for help.

A Monster lived in the forest. He heard her and came out of his cave. Lily was shocked to see him. She closed her eyes, turned back and ran as fast as she could.

She opened her eyes after running a long distance and saw her Father standing in front of her. She hugged him and apologised for not listening to him.

20. Grumpy Nancy

Nancy, the grumpy fairy lived in fairyland. She found faults with everyone.

One day, she went to buy some bread. The Baker Fairy gave her the best bread, but Nancy told her, "The bread does not look good! It seems you don't know how to bake bread."

The Baker Fairy said, "You are very rude. I don't want to talk to you."

Similarly, Nancy spoke rudely to all the other fairies and upset them. They stopped talking and doing any work for her.

Now, Nancy had to do all the work on her own. Also, she felt sad and lonely.

After a few days, she went to the Queen Fairy and complained.

The Queen Fairy said, "Nobody wants to be friends with a grumpy person. If you show love and respect to others, they will also show love to you."

Nancy realised her mistake and improved her behaviour. Soon, everybody forgave her and started talking to her again.

21. Snowfall

Lily, Ann, Daisy and Pearl were best friends. One day, Pearl invited her friends for lunch.

The girls enjoyed the lunch and went to Pearl's room. It was still afternoon but was dark outside due to snowfall. Suddenly, the candles went out and it became dark in the house, too.

The girls got scared and held each other's hands, while Pearl's Mother guided them to the sitting room.

Pearl's Father lit the fireplace to keep the room warm. He said, "All the roads have been blocked due to the snowfall. So, none of you can go back home tonight."

Lily, Ann and Daisy got really worried. But Pearl's Mother assured, "I have informed your parents about this."

Now, the girls were relaxed. Soon, Pearl's Mother got some drinks and snacks. They spent the entire night talking and because of each other's company, they could enjoy even in the bad weather.

22. Lazy Shirley

Shirley lived with her parents. She never liked to do any work. Her Mother did the entire household work but Shirley never offered to help.

One day, her Mother said, "You must learn household work. How will you manage if you're alone?" Shirley did not bother.

After many years, she went to study at the university and had to stay in the hostel. All her roommates did their work themselves, but Shirley did not know anything.

She could not lay her bed, wash and iron her clothes or polish her shoes. Her classmates continuously poked fun at her for wearing dirty clothes and shoes.

Now, Shirley realised that she should have listened to her Mother. So, she requested her roommates to guide her.

Her roommates were surprised, but liked her effort to learn. Soon, Shirley learnt and surprised her Mother in the holidays! Her Mother was also very happy.

23. Naughty Girls

Tracy, Maggie and Sara were best friends. One weekend, Sara's parents had gone to her grandparents' house. So, the friends decided to sleep over at Sara's house.

At night, they went to Sara's room and danced for a long time.

Maggie and Sara started dancing on the bed. Tracy warned them, "You should not jump on the bed. It might break." But, they did not listen.

Suddenly, the bed broke and Maggie and Sara fell down. Tracy helped them get up.

Now, Sara started crying. She was scared that her parents would scold her for being so naughty.

Sara's Brother heard the noise and came to her room. He was shocked to see the broken bed. He comforted his sister and said, "Don't cry, I can mend this for you."

Then, Sara's Brother got the toolbox and mended the bed. She and Maggie promised, never to be naughty again.

24. Sleepy Princess

Once, a Princess lived in a large and beautiful palace. One day, she was playing in the garden with her friends. Their noise disturbed a spirit sleeping on the tree.

He woke up in rage and said, "Silly Princess! How dare you disturb my sleep? I curse you that you will never be able to sleep in peace from now on."

From then on, the Princess could not sleep at night. So, she went to the balcony and counted the stars to pass the night.

The Queen Fairy saw her growing pale due to lack of sleep. She pitied her and requested a Fairy to bless her and remove her curse.

The Fairy went to the Princess and said, "I will remove your curse, if you promise to be good and never disturb anybody."

The Princess promised and the Fairy blessed her. Since then, the Princess could sleep in peace every night. And she also fulfilled her promise of not disturbing anyone.

25. Ellie's Little Sister

Ellie lived with her parents in a beautiful house. One day, her parents brought her baby sister home. Now, Ellie's Mother spent most of her time with the baby. Her Father brought new toys and clothes for the baby.

Ellie's relatives also came home and showered their love on the baby. Ellie felt left out and cried all day in her room.

One day, Ellie's Father heard her cry and told her Mother, "Ellie is upset because of us. We should talk to her."

Then, the parents took the baby in Ellie's room. The Mother made Ellie sit in her lap and asked, "Did you not want a sister when your friends played with their brothers and sisters?"

Ellie said, "Yes, I always wanted to have a sister to play with."

So, the Father said, "Here is your sister!"

Now, Ellie stopped feeling left out and kissed her little sister.

26. Sleepy Betty

Betty lived with her parents. She had one bad habit. She always made some excuse to sleep till late.

Every day, her Mother shouted, "Get up Betty, otherwise you will miss your school bus." But, Betty would not listen.

Betty often missed her school bus and her Father had to drop her to school. But, she did not seem to bother.

One day, Betty's Father was not at home. As usual, she got late and missed her bus. Her Mother hired a taxi and dropped her to the school, but the gates of the school were closed by then.

Betty had a painting competition that day. She requested the guards to let her in, but they refused. So, she had to go back home with her Mother.

Betty loved painting and missed the competition due to her bad habit.

She realised her mistake and woke up on time thereafter.

27. Percy's Grandfather

Percy lived with her parents. One day, they had to go out of town for some work.

Percy's Mother told her, "While we are away, you will have to stay with your Grandfather." Percy was upset. She did not want to stay with him. He lived alone and Percy thought she would be bored.

But, her parents dropped her at her Grandfather's house. Percy went inside and was surprised to see many toys! Her Grandfather knew she was coming, so had bought toys for her.

Percy was really happy, now. Grandfather played with her all day. He taught her gardening and painting. He took her to the local museum and the park for picnic.

After a few days, when Percy's parents came to take her, she did not want to go. She said, "I love Grandpa and will stay with him."

Then, Grandfather explained, "You will have to go back now. But, you can visit me in your holidays."

Percy agreed and went home with her parents.

28. Rachel Caught the Spirits

Rachel had few good friends in the school. One day, they decided to sleep over at Rachel's house.

Rachel took permission from her parents and organised a tent in the garden to sleep. All the friends were very excited.

After dinner, they moved into the tent. They gathered snacks and decided to stay up till late night.

Rachel and her friends played games and sang songs. Suddenly, they heard some sounds. One of them said, "I can see something moving behind the trees."

Another one agreed and screamed, "Oh God! It is a spirit."

All the friends got scared but Rachel said, "No spirit lives in my garden. Do not get scared and let me check."

Rachel got up and went behind the tree. She came out with two boys of her class. They had come there to scare the girls. Instead, they were caught and punished by the girls!

29. Stubborn Tina

Tina lived with her parents in a beautiful house. She was very stubborn and did not listen to anybody.

One day, she and her friends made a plan to go for a picnic on the weekend. She told her Mother about it.

Mother said, "I will let you go, only if you promise to be good this entire week." Tina promised her Mother.

Next day, it started raining in the afternoon. Tina loved rains and ran out in the garden. Her Mother shouted, "Tina, come back, otherwise you'll fall sick."

Tina did not bother and played in the rain. At night, she was sneezing with cold and had high fever.

The Doctor advised her to rest for a few days.

On the weekend, Tina's friends went for the picnic, but Tina could not accompany them. The friends had lots of fun and told Tina about it. She felt very bad about not listening to her Mother.

30. The Reward of Patience

"Mother," Kate said, "I want to become a painter!"

Mother asked, "Why?"

Kate said, "A famous artist visited our school today, with his paintings. Mother, they simply filled my heart with joy!"

Opening a cupboard, Mother took out a box with Kate's name on it. She handed Kate a sheet of paper from the box.

"Remember when you wanted to become a famous writer?" she asked. Kate looked at the sheet of paper with the story she had never completed.

"Last year you wanted to be a ballerina. Before that, a space scientist!" The ballet shoes Kate had adored were now dirty. The telescope her father had given her was covered in dust.

Mother said kindly, "My darling, your excitement about doing something great is wonderful. But when the excitement ends, you must finish what you had started. Seeing your finished work will be the most beautiful reward ever!"

1. No Secrets!

The girls were in school. The bell rang. All the girls came out of their classrooms. Some girls stood in a group and whispered to each other.

Kate wanted to know what they were talking about. So, she went to them and asked, "Megan, can you tell me what you are talking about?"

Megan replied, "Sure Kate, if you promise not to tell your Mother."

Kate was a good girl. She told her Mother everything that happened. So, the girls did not tell Kate any of their secrets.

Kate said, "Megan, I tell my Mother everything. If I cannot tell her, it means I cannot know it either."

Megan said, "Kate, it is alright if you don't tell your Mother some things. These are girl secrets. They have to be with the girls."

Kate replied, "Sorry Megan, I don't have to know your secrets. I share all my 'girl' secrets with my Mother." And she walked away.

2. Hansel and Gretel

Once, there lived two children; a boy named Hansel and his sister, Gretel. Their Father was a poor Woodcutter and Stepmother a cruel woman.

One day, Hansel and Gretel heard their Stepmother say, "Let's leave the children in the forest, as we are left with very little food." The Woodcutter was saddened, but kept quiet before his cunning wife.

The next morning, their Stepmother played a trick and left them in the forest. Poor children! They wandered in the forest for many days.

Then, to their delight, they found a hut. The roof, chimney, windows, doors; all were made of delicious cakes and biscuits! They were hungry and sat down eating the windows and the roof!

The hut belonged to a dreadful but half-blind Witch. She caught Hansel and Gretel and screamed, "I shall fatten this thin boy first and cook him for my feast!"

Every day, when the Witch used to touch Hansel's fingers to see if he had grown fat, Gretel would place her thin finger in front of the Witch. The Witch, being half-blind would scream, "Oh! This boy is still as thin as bamboo."

One day, the Witch was annoyed. "This boy is taking too long to become fat. I shall not wait!"

She asked Gretel to heat up the oven. What could Gretel do? Suddenly, an idea struck her. She told the Witch that she did not know how to heat the oven. When the Witch bent close to the oven, Gretel pushed her inside. The Witch herself was baked!

Hansel and Gretel collected the jewels hidden inside the hut. Then, they found their way back home. The Woodcutter was delighted to see his children. With the jewels that the children had picked up, they were poor no more.

3. Sweet Emily

There was once a girl named Emily. She was a well-behaved and helpful child.

One day, Emily went out to the park to play. There were already some children playing in the park. They all took turns playing on the swings and the slide.

Sarah was a little girl who loved the swings. But she could not reach it. She needed help. She asked Emily, "Can you help me on the swings?"

Emily happily helped Sarah to get on the swing and pushed her. Sarah and Emily loved playing together.

Once, when Emily pushed Sarah, the little girl lost control and fell from the swing. She got hurt and started crying. The other children saw this and ran away, scared. They thought that they would be scolded.

Emily was scared too. But, she ran to help Sarah. Sarah cried, "My knee hurts. I want to go home to Mother."

Emily said, "Oh! Hold my hand and I'll take you home." And she gently took Sarah home to her Mother. Sarah's Mother did not scold Emily. In fact, she thanked her for bringing her injured daughter home!

4. The Two Sisters

Emma and Sophie were sisters. Emma was a quiet girl and loved to read. She never went out to play.

Sophie was just the opposite. She was always outside, playing with her friends. She never spent any time at home.

Their Mother said, "Emma, you should go outside and play with Sophie for some time. And Sophie, you should learn to sit down and read for at least an hour every day."

So, Emma decided to go out to play with Sophie. Sophie showed her a lot of fun games that Emma never knew about. Emma enjoyed playing outdoors.

Then, when they came home, Sophie said, "Emma can you help me pick a book to read?"

Emma said, "Let's read together, Sophie. This is a very funny book."

The sisters enjoyed reading the book. They understood how much fun it was to play with each other. Their Mother was very happy.

5. A Day at the Beach

Elizabeth went to the beach with her Mother and Father.

Elizabeth loved building sand castles with her Father. So, the two of them started building a castle. They dug deep into the sand using a shovel. Now, they had a lot of wet sand. They used pails to make blocks of sand and stacked them up to make towers.

Elizabeth said, "Father, these towers look so beautiful! Can we build walls around the castle?"

"Sure, Elizabeth," said Father and he helped build the walls. Then, Elizabeth used her plastic utensils to shape the tower and walls.

The sand castle was beautiful. Elizabeth said, "This is the best castle, Father. It is so beautiful."

Father agreed, "Yes dear. You did a very good job shaping up those walls."

Mother was very happy to see Elizabeth enjoy. She took a photograph of the sand castle to put up in their living room. She knew that when Elizabeth grew up, she would miss playing with her Father… but the memories and the photograph will make her happy!

6. Garden Fairies

Jenny lived in a cottage. She had a lovely garden outside the cottage. A few fairies lived in Jenny's garden. The Flower Fairy coloured all the flowers and gave them their fragrance. One day, she fell ill and was advised to take rest. The Queen Fairy said, "I will assign your work to Flounder and Mischief, two other fairies."

Now, Flounder and Mischief were very naughty. They coloured the bluebells yellow and the sunflowers blue. Also, they made the roses smell like jasmine!

Next morning, Jenny went to the garden and was shocked. She immediately called the Flower Fairy. When the Flower Fairy saw her garden in such a mess, she went and complained to the Queen Fairy.

The Queen ordered to make everything in the garden normal like before. So, the bluebells were blue and sunflowers were yellow, again. Also, the roses and jasmine got their own fragrances back.

Jenny was happy now.

7. Sand Castle

Jessica was at the beach with her friends. They had built a beautiful sand castle. Sadly, a huge wave came by and washed off the sand castle. The girls were all very upset.

Jessica cried, "It was such a beautiful castle. Why did the wave wash off our castle?"

Melanie was a very sensible girl. She said, "Jessica, sand castles do not last forever. They do get washed away sometimes. Please do not cry."

However, Jessica and the other girls were sad. Melanie said, "Girls, I have taken a picture of the sand castle. Come let's go to the store and print the picture."

The girls were now excited. They went with Melanie and got the picture printed. The picture had all the girls and their sand castle. It was perfect!

Everyone was happy to see the picture. Melanie gave them each a copy. Jessica said, "Thanks Melanie, this is a great idea. I think we should always take pictures of what we build; after all, nothing lasts forever!"

8. New Friends

Andrea and Alice were sisters. Andrea was eleven and Alice was five years old. Alice followed her sister all the time. Andrea was tired of Alice following her. She did not want Alice to be there when she was playing with her friends.

One day, Andrea and her friends were playing a board game. As always, Alice wanted to play with them. But Andrea said, "Alice why don't you play something else when I play with my friends?"

Alice said, "But, I am bored! Please let me play with you. It's fun."

Andrea replied, "It's time you had your own friends," and called out to their Mother.

"Mother," she said, "I want to play with my friends. Please ask Alice to go away."

Mother understood the situation. She told Alice, "Alice let's go out and see if Rebecca wants to play."

Alice went with Mother to play with Rebecca.

9. Obedient Children

Rosaline and Rita were sisters. Their Mother was very poor. Their Father was not alive and so Mother had to work hard.

Rita and Rosaline helped Mother, as they knew she worked hard.

One day, their neighbour Mrs. Smith was taking her children to the park for a picnic. She was a very nice lady. She asked, "Would you girls like to join us for the picnic?"

Rita said, "I shall ask my Mother when she is back."

Rita and Rosaline were very excited about the picnic. They knew Mother would not mind if they went with Mrs. Smith.

So, they ran to their garden and collected a basket of fruits. Then, they waited for their Mother. When Mother came back home, they asked her if they could go with Mrs. Smith for the picnic.

Mother agreed and thanked Mrs. Smith for her kindness. She also packed some hard-boiled eggs along with the fruits, for the picnic.

10. Helping and Thanksgiving

It was Thanksgiving. Mrs. Bogart was busy cooking a traditional meal. Her sister's family was coming for dinner. Mrs. Bogart had two children, Ruby and Ruth. They asked, "Mother, we can't wait to see our guests. When will they come?"

Mrs. Bogart said, "They will be here at dinner time. Their children will also come. You will meet your cousins, today."

Ruby and Ruth picked out good clothes to wear for the dinner. Then, they asked Mother to help them get dressed. Mother said, "Why don't you girls first help me set the table?"

Ruby said, "Mother, can the children eat at a different table?"

"Sure, dear," said Mother. "You can take the children's plates from the bottom drawer and set your table."

Ruby and Ruth set the table and then Mother helped them get dressed. It was going to be the best Thanksgiving they ever had! It was a good feeling to get all dressed up and have your own special table laid out for dinner!

11. Decorating a Tree

It was December. Father took the girls to buy a Christmas tree. Martha and Magda went with their Dad to the tree farm. They walked around looking for a good tree. The tree-seller had a variety of trees in different sizes.

Martha saw a short tree and said, "Father, can we please buy this?" Father and Magda like it, too. And they bought that tree. Father set the tree up in the house and said, "Martha and Magda, now you girls have to decorate the tree."

The girls were happy. They opened up the box of decorations that they had collected over the years. It was full of colourful lights, ribbons and streamers.

There were colourful bells of different sizes too. The two sisters hung up all the decorations. They tied a bright, red-beaded garland around the tree. And finally, they put up a bright twinkling star on the top of the tree.

It was the best Christmas tree ever! It was indeed very sensible to have saved up all those decorations over the years!

12. Fishing a Fish

Sally loved fishing with her Father. It was her favourite pastime.

On her seventh Birthday, her Mother got her a fishing kit. It had a cute pink rod and a pink hat. Then, Father took Sally to the farm pond to fish. Once, they reached the pond, Sally put on her pink cap and took her fishing rod. She sat by the edge of the pond with her Father. Father said, "Sally, you have to be patient and concentrate really well."

Though Sally was very excited, yet she remained calm. She could not wait to catch the first fish, using her new rod; but waited patiently to do so.

Suddenly, the light on her new fishing rod turned on and she felt a slight pull. Sally knew that there was something on the hook. She immediately pulled out the rod.

It was a small fish. Sally happily showed her catch to the other people who were fishing at the pond! They all admired the little girl, who had so much patience, so as to catch a fish.

13. Proud Jade

Once, a beautiful mermaid, Jade lived in the sea. She was very proud of her beauty.

So, everyone disliked her except the Giant Turtle. He followed her wherever she went, to protect her. But, Jade never bothered about him.

One day, she heard some mermaids talk about a pirate ship that had sunk in the sea. They said, "The ship has many beautiful, but cursed, jewels."

Jade thought, 'I must get those jewels.' Then, she left to find the jewels in the ship.

Jade found a big box full of gold and diamonds on the ship. She picked up a necklace and wore it. Suddenly, the gold necklace turned to stone and became extremely heavy.

Now, Jade could not move. She started crying. And promptly, the Giant Turtle came and broke the stone necklace to free Jade.

Jade thanked him and decided to be friendly and humble in the future.

14. Naughty Mermaids

The mermaids, Fizz and Jazz were very naughty. One day, they saw a boy, Jack standing on the lighthouse. They called him and hid under the water when he tried to look.

Soon, Jack got tired. He sat down on a rock and opened his lunch box. The mermaids smelt food and came to him. They requested, "Can we also share the food with you?"

Jack shared his lunch with them. Once, the mermaids were full, they decided to go back.

But, they could not move. Then, they remembered their Mother's words, "Mermaids cannot eat the food meant for humans."

Now, Fizz and Jazz started crying. They requested Jack for help. Jack went and got a net. Then, he collected the food for mermaids from the sea and gave it to them.

The mermaids ate and were finally able to move, again. They thanked Jack and went back to the sea.

15. Brave Princess

Once, a Princess wanted to marry the neighbouring Prince, but he refused her marriage proposal. The Princess was heartbroken.

A few days later, she requested her Father, "Please let me go for hunting, today." Soon, the Princess left the guards behind and was alone in the forest.

Suddenly, she heard a cry. She found that a Man had fallen into a deep pit. She took out a rope and started pulling the Man out.

Within minutes, a tiger came in front of the Princess. The Man was sure that she would get scared and leave the rope to run away.

But, the Princess continued and pulled the Man out of the pit.

Surprisingly, the tiger did not attack any of them and left. When, the Princess saw the Man, she recognised him as the neighbouring Prince. He apologised to her.

Soon, they got married and lived happily ever after.

16. Poor Shoemaker

Once, a poor Shoemaker and his Wife lived in a small cottage. One day, he could not complete an order, due to fever.

His Wife got really worried, as the client was going to come the next day to take his shoes.

Next morning, the Shoemaker and his Wife were shocked to see the shoes made. The client came and paid a good price for them.

The Shoemaker and his Wife wondered, "Who made the shoes at night?"

They decided to keep a watch. At midnight, they saw, two Elves enter from the window and complete the Shoemaker's orders.

The next day, the Shoemaker and his Wife made two pair of clothes and little shoes for the Elves and kept them on the table.

The Elves came and saw their gifts. They were extremely happy. After that, they made sure that the Shoemaker and his Wife never faced any trouble.

17. Sugarplum

Sugarplum was the kindest fairy in fairyland. One day, the Queen Fairy called her and said, "Dear, I want you to stitch a rose petal gown for my birthday party."

Sugarplum said, "I will definitely make the most beautiful gown for you."

Then, Sugarplum started gathering roses for the gown. Suddenly, she saw a Butterfly with a broken wing on a flower. Sugarplum took pity on it and decided to mend her wing with magic.

Soon, the Butterfly recovered and was fit to fly, but Sugarplum felt very sad. The Butterfly asked her, "Why are you so sad?"

Sugarplum replied, "I will not be able to stitch the Queen's gown in time, since I got busy mending your wing."

Within minutes, the Butterfly called all her friends and helped Sugarplum make the most beautiful gown for the Queen.

The Queen Fairy appreciated Sugarplum's work before the entire fairyland.

18. Two Cheats

Once, a Queen lived in her palace. One day, she announced, "If somebody brings me some exotic cloth for my gown, I will give him a big reward."

Two Cheats lived in her kingdom.

They went to the court and pretended to be holding a piece of cloth. Then, they said, "A fool's eye might find it invisible, but we can make a beautiful gown for you out of this." The Queen gave them permission to stitch a gown.

A few days later, the two men came, pretending to be holding a delicate gown and said, "Dear Queen, this is for you."

The Queen, too, pretended to take the invisible gown. Then, she gave them an empty bag and said, "These are very special coins. They might look invisible to a fool, but are worth millions."

The Cheats understood that the Queen had caught them and ran away from the palace, before the guards caught them!

19. Alice's Spots

Alice was a princess. She was cursed by a witch and had spots all over her face. This made Alice look very ugly. She remained sad and never went out of her room.

Every night, when everyone was asleep, she covered her face and went on to the terrace. She liked to watch the moon.

One night, she saw a few fairies around the moon. She closed her eyes and prayed, "Dear fairies, please be kind and make me beautiful."

All the fairies ignored her except one, the Clementine Fairy. Clementine went to her and said, "Dear child, you are kind and have a pure heart. So, I will help you."

She gave Alice a magic drink. Alice drank it and slept. Next morning, she awoke and saw no spots on her face! Clementine had made her very pretty.

Alice thanked her and finally came out of her room.

20. Meg

Molly was a sheepdog and helped the Farmer keep a track of his sheep. The Farmer always praised Molly for her work.

Molly's daughter, Meg watched her work and wanted to help. But, Molly felt that she was too young to work.

One day, Molly was helping the Farmer to put all the sheep into a big pen. "Good girl, Molly!" said the Farmer, closing the gate and patting her on the head.

Suddenly, Meg saw a lamb slip through a crack in the gate and run away. Meg barked to inform but Molly and the Farmer did not notice.

So, Meg ran behind the lamb and saw it stuck in a hedge. Then, she went back and led the Farmer forcefully to the hedge. The Farmer took the lamb home. Then, he said, "Good girl, Meg!"

Meg was very happy that she had helped the Farmer, too! And Molly did not feel that Meg was young any more!

21. Emily's Best Friend

Emily lived with her parents in a lovely house. She had a beautiful garden and played with her best friend, Daisy, in that garden, all day.

One day, Emily's Father got a lovely doll for her. Emily named her, Dolly, and took great care of her.

A few days later, Daisy saw Dolly and wanted to play with her. But, Emily refused to give it. Daisy got upset and went back to her house. Emily felt very bad and started crying. Her Mother asked, "What is the matter, Emily?"

Emily told her the entire story. Mother smiled and asked, "Is Daisy your best friend or Dolly?"

Emily replied, "Daisy is my best friend."

Now, Mother said, "Then, you should not have hurt your best friend for anybody, not even for your favourite doll."

Emily understood and took Dolly to Daisy's house. Both the girls played with the doll all day.

22. The Enchanted Garden

Princess Sylvie went for a walk every evening.

One day, she came across a path with beautiful flowers on both sides. She asked a Woman nearby, "What place does this path lead to?"

The Woman replied, "It leads to the garden of an Enchantress. If you are going there, do not pick any flowers."

Sylvie wanted to see the garden. She reached there and was surprised to see so many flowers everywhere. Soon, she forgot the warning and plucked a big red rose for herself.

Suddenly, the entire garden dried up and she heard the Enchantress cry aloud. Sylvie reached the Enchantress' cottage. She asked, "Why are you crying?"

The Enchantress replied, "Somebody plucked a flower from my garden. And so, the garden has completely dried and can be restored only if a princess waters it."

Sylvie realised her mistake and watered the entire garden. Soon, the garden was green and beautiful again.

23. Christmas Presents

It was Christmas Eve. The Smith family had put up their glorious, six feet tall, Christmas tree in the living room. It was decorated with fir and pine cones, coloured eggshells, and different shapes cut out of craft paper. The shapes looked like snowflakes. There was a beautiful star on the top of the tree.

In the evening, the Smith family enjoyed a delicious six-course dinner. Grace and Bella helped their mother clean up after dinner. Then, they hung up their stockings and left cookies and milk by the fireplace for Santa Claus. They went to bed, hoping Santa would leave presents for them.

Grace and Bella's parents knew that they had been good children all year. After the girls were asleep, they put big presents under the Christmas tree for them. In the morning, Grace and Bella were very happy. They decided to be good children next year, too.

24. Naughty Lizzie

Lizzie lived with her parents and little brother. She was very naughty and was scolded all day by her Mother.

One day, she pinched her brother while he was asleep. He got up and cried. Lizzie's Mother locked her in the room.

After some time, Lizzie's Grandmother came home. Lizzie heard her Mother complain about her to the Grandmother. She was very ashamed.

Then, Grandmother came to her room. She said, "You should not do all these naughty things, my child. Everybody will love you if you learn to behave."

Now, Lizzie decided to be a good girl. She went to school on time and studied hard.

Also, Lizzie did all her homework and helped her Mother with the household tasks. Her parents were pleasantly surprised with her behaviour.

They bought her many new toys. Lizzie was very happy and thought, 'Being good really pays off!'

25. Christmas Magic

Anna and her Mother lived in a village where there was no doctor. Anna always saw that people suffered so much. Also, Anna's Mother was very poor.

Once, Anna's rich Aunt visited them from town. She asked Anna's Mother to send Anna with her. Anna's Mother refused, but Anna wanted to go. So, Anna's Mother bid her goodbye.

Many years passed. It was Christmas! Anna's Mother sat all alone in her house. She was unwell and missed Anna, terribly. Just then, a beautiful Lady walked into the house in a doctor's white coat and stethoscope.

She said, "Merry Christmas Mother, it is me, Anna. I hated leaving you alone, but I knew you had to work very hard for me. Then, I decided to be a doctor by studying hard. Now, I am back forever!"

Anna's Mother hugged her tight and said, "This is the best Christmas ever!"

26. Ashley's Brother

Ashley had a very naughty brother, Max. He troubled Ashley all the time and played many pranks on her.

One day, Max and his friends hung a bucket full of ice-cold water on the door. They tied it with a string and decided to pull the string as soon as Ashley entered the room, so that the water would fall on her.

When Max heard Ashley come near the room, he climbed on the chair to pull the string. But, he could not maintain his balance and fell down from the chair. All the water fell on him and he caught cold and fever.

Now, he had to stay in bed for a few days. Ashley felt very bad for her brother and did as much as she could to look after him, to get him well soon.

Max was very touched and apologised to his sister. He never played any pranks on her again.

27. The Joy of Christmas

Nellie and Adele were decorating the Christmas tree in their living room. Nellie said, "Have you made your Christmas wish?"

"I have written to Santa, but I won't tell you!" Adele said.

The girls were very excited that Christmas was almost there. When they hung up all the decorations on the tree, Nellie said, "Let's make cards for our friends!"

So, the girls started making cards for each of their friends, wishing them a Happy Christmas and New Year. They used bright paints and craft paper.

Then, Adele said, "Nellie, now I am making one for you. But you have to wait until Christmas to open it."

"I'll make one for you, too. You will be surprised when you see it!" said Nellie.

Laughing, the two girls finished their cards and went to bed. Both were very happy and understood that the true spirit of Christmas was sharing and caring.

28. Mina's Lucky Shoes

Mina went for her dance class every week. She learnt ballet with great dedication.

But, for the past few days, Mina was very upset. She practised to spin on one foot, day and night, but was not able to get it right.

After a while, she refused to go for the ballet class. Her Mother asked, "What is stopping you from dancing?"

She replied, "Mother, I have not been able to get my spin right, even after weeks of practice."

Her Mother took out a pair of lovely ballet shoes. Then, she said, "These are my lucky ballet shoes. I won many competitions, when I danced wearing them, in my childhood days."

Mina wore the shoes to her dance class. Surprisingly, she did all her spins perfectly well. Her Teacher was also very happy.

Mina came home and hugged her Mother. She thanked her and said, "They are indeed the luckiest shoes."

29. The Elf's Gift

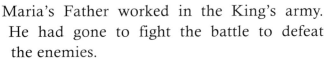

Maria's Father worked in the King's army. He had gone to fight the battle to defeat the enemies.

One day, Maria found a bottle on the beach. She opened the cork and lo, a tiny Elf jumped out! He said, "You saved my life! Ask me for one wish!"

Maria wanted a pretty doll but she said, "Can I think and tell you tomorrow?"

The Elf agreed and Maria went home. Her Mother was waiting for her at home. Teary-eyed, she told her that her Father had been wounded at the battlefield. Maria started crying and prayed to God.

The next day, she ran to the beach and said to the Elf, "Please save my Father's life! Please bring him back home!"

The Elf quietly vanished. Maria sadly returned home. When she reached home, her Father was actually lying on the bed. Maria jumped with joy and hugged him, tight.

30. God Listens To Us All

It was Christmas and a poor little girl, Ness, was sitting at her window. Ness lived with her Aunt, who did not treat her very well.

Through the window, Ness saw a family celebrating Christmas across the street. They had a beautiful tree and gifts and everybody wore new clothes. Ness saw the children's Mother and wondered how it felt to have a Mother, for she had never seen her own Mother!

Ness felt so sad that she started to cry. Soon, she fell asleep and saw a dream. She saw her Mother, who said, "Ness, I am always with you!"

Ness woke up suddenly and saw that there were gifts all around her. There was a note that said, "We are always with you and we love you."

God had listened to Ness' wishes and had sent Santa Claus with the gifts for Ness. Ness never felt sad ever again!

31. Crystal's New Year

Crystal was a beautiful fairy who lived near the rainbow. She had long golden hair, blue eyes and wore pink robes. She was also very kind.

One day, as Crystal was flying in the village, she saw a little Girl and her Mother. The Girl was crying, "I have tried for three hundred and sixty five days! I will never be able to bake a cake!"

Her Mother said, "No dear, you should keep trying more."

Crystal felt very bad for the little Girl. She said, "After trying for three hundred and sixty five days, you should celebrate and try again! When you do this, you will be in the New Year! It will keep you happy."

The Girl was pleased now. She said, "I want a Happy New Year. I will try to succeed every day and celebrate after three hundred and sixty five days!"

Since then, people started celebrating New Year.